THE CHILD OF MONTMARTRE

Paul Léautaud was born in 1872 and died in 1955 at the age of eighty-three. He was the illegitimate son of the prompter at the Comédie-Française and a minor actress. He wrote relatively little, but when his short autobiographical novel *Le Petit Ami* and its two related pieces, here published under the general title of *The Child of Montmartre*, appeared in the early years of the century they aroused a mixture of admiration for the literary ability they displayed and shocked surprise at their frankness.

Mr Graham Green writes of the book: 'He has taken for his own a particular area of human life and no one is his rival there. It was the same area that Toulouse-Lautrec painted: the bars and brothels of Montmartre, the ugly, the beautiful and ravaged faces of the ageing cocottes. He "judges not as a judge judges": he only notices with the clear curious impartial eye of a child.'

THE CHILD OF
MONTMARTRE

———

PAUL LÉAUTAUD

TRANSLATED FROM THE FRENCH BY

Humphrey Hare

RANDOM HOUSE
NEW YORK

Le Petit Ami, Paris 1902
In Memoriam, Paris 1905
Amours, Paris 1906
[reprinted in one volume, Paris 1956]
The Child of Montmartre, London and New York 1959

Contents

PART I

Le Petit Ami

---

*The extremes of
passion look silly when written.*
STENDHAL

To

HENRI DE RÉGNIER

PART I : LE PETIT AMI

Chapter I

In life there are only beginnings.

MME DE STAEL

One evening, a few years ago, I was in a famous music-hall with some friends; I can still see the big hall, with its tables and chairs, the promenade round it, the two galleries on either side, the stage at the end, and the communicating door on the right leading into the auditorium. As usual, there was quite a collection of those women of whom it is said there are none like them in other capitals, at least as far as grace and elegance are concerned. As for the rest of the crowd, it consisted of foreigners, loungers like ourselves, old beaux and young people, with a few bourgeois. In short, the usual lot, not forgetting the waiters, with their stumbling gait resembling that of Little Tich.

I have rather forgotten which of my friends were with me that night. They must have been some of my comrades on the *Revue* whom I had found there by chance. As for me, I had been going to some such place every night for some time past, to the Folies-Bergère or the Jardin de Paris, according to the time of year. Emerging from my serious reading, I found relaxation in these colourful places; life in them was many-hued, after the inert, monotonous masterpieces; and I found them all the more grateful because, lounging there, I got to know several of the women who frequented them. I chatted with them and was often in their company.

We joined a circle of spectators round three or four girls

dancing with considerable abandon; they lacked neither grace nor immodesty; then we went and sat at a table by the little salon near the entrance. The interplay of dresses, of faces and gestures continued nearby beneath the thousands of lights, as if the spectacle had been spontaneously generated for us alone. What reveries occupied my mind that night, reveries emerging from a distant past to which I could give no precise form! For a moment, a woman stood near us, having stopped to talk to another woman and some men; she was really very attractive. My friends and I gazed at her in silence, they merely casually perhaps, but I with interest. 'It really is a great pity my mother was not more ambitious,' I remarked after a moment, without thinking what I was saying. 'With her talents, she would be much in vogue today, and I should enjoy the benefit of her luxury and her circle of friends.'

I repeat, I was not really thinking what I was saying. Perhaps, indeed, I had spoken unconsciously, impelled to it by an obscure and pleasurable emotion. But friends are not friends for nothing. I had hardly uttered the words when they began vying with each other in abusing me. I was affected, I was depraved, I was a compromising, even a hopeless character, etc. But I was still so taken up with the woman standing nearby that it never occurred to me even for a second to answer them back. In any case, it was better so. Courteous as I am, it would have been somewhat embarrassing to have to point out to these young men that, by flattering me in this way, they were lacking in manners.

In a way, it was really that evening that the idea of one day writing this book occurred to me. Having given vent to their noble rage, my friends left me. We had almost come to the last tunes. There was no one left but here and there a few of these charming women who, not yet booked, were yawning among themselves, and a few loungers without money or without desire. The sight of them gave me food for serious reflection till the place closed. Though I constantly watched myself acting and dreaming I had never thought about myself so much before. It led me to the recollection of my childhood. From it came, undoubtedly, my liking for these disparaged women of whom a little while ago I had made the mistake of thinking aloud. I remembered those happy years, spent among somewhat similar creatures, who lifted me up in their arms to kiss me and at whose coquetry I marvelled. How natural it was that I should now take pleasure in their company: I was only continuing to be the little boy I had once been, and the feelings they inspired in me, though now perhaps somewhat shocking, had already been implanted in him. I told myself, too, that I was doing nothing and, since novels and poems no longer attracted me, I ought to try to write something about all that. I had many memories already, I could complete them; I had also talked a good deal to the few women I knew; I had even been to see two or three of them at home and had dined with several; I needed only to go on and cherish these relationships: with a mixture of work and idleness, all this might one day make a tolerable book. I began to envisage the chapters, the tone of each, the approximate number of pages, and the agreeable hours of preparation. All this seemed such a good idea that, by the time I left, I had made up my mind: I would write this book, but only when it would give me pleasure to do so.

Before beginning work, I began by being idle, garnering memories, frequenting these women more than ever on random evenings, and sometimes spending afternoons at home boring myself to death making notes that were to be of no use to me. This went on for several years, for I could not make up my mind where to begin. What long faces my young Catos would pull when they read the record of the pleasures of my heart! But above all I thought of the delight of my women friends when one idle day I would read them these pages full of themselves and of me.

I therefore write this book, consisting for the most part of memories, without really knowing whether it will give pleasure. That will depend on so many things I cannot foresee! Had I two or three friends who did not write themselves, I would perhaps send it to them to read and tell me what they thought. I should make no corrections, for nothing is so boring as beginning things over again, but at least I should acquire a little information on the point. However lacking in enthusiasm one may be for one's own work, it is so easy to make an error of judgment. One should put the manuscript away in a drawer and wait a year at least.

Anyway, even if it bores the reader, I hope the book won't bore my women friends, accustomed as they are to my egotism. As soon as they knew that I intended writing a book in which they appeared, they encouraged me as much as they could. I even still have in a drawer the photographs they gave me for reproduction, if I thought proper, in appropriate places. These are attentions one does not forget. They also often asked me where I had got to in my work, if I was pleased with it, whether it was going well. 'How's it coming along?' they used to say. This was more particularly during the period when I was preparing myself with the ardour I have described above. Touched by their questions, I used to reply that, thank Heaven, it wasn't coming along too badly at the moment! Then they would leave me in peace for a few days, only to begin again, always avid for details: what was I saying about them, was it a really serious work? etc. I had quite a little public in prospect.

Delightful hours, in which I was full of assurance! Besides, it is always the same: when far from my papers, I feel as if I have genius, but when it's a question of getting down to work, goodbye, there's nothing there at all! At the moment, I am thinking of all the things I want to put in this book, things that will perhaps deserve the admiration of my family. I am thinking of the little boy I was, so long ago now, and whom I still resemble so closely. I recall the faces of those I have left but yesterday and the vanished faces to which I once put my lips, and the gaiety or the silence of places in which I have lingered. And finally I think of my mother, whom it appears I resemble so much in character, and whom I saw once, when I was about ten, in circumstances I shall never forget. How little I know of her: only what my father told me on occasion (that she was small but had a beautiful figure), my childhood memories of her, two or three words dropped by a relation, and a few photographs I have of her. . . . Oh, don't interrupt me, I pray you, in this elegiac and reminiscent mood! Heavens, suppose I began taking myself seriously, even unintentionally! I, and others, have been reproached so often for our lack of interest in the fate of the Motherland, in the parliamentary and municipal elections, in the birth- and death-rates, and in all the various economic, sociological, patriotic and feminist problems! Moreover, my women friends have learned to be suspicious. They have heard so much meaningless flattery, so many promises that have not been kept, that they look twice before approving. 'What a lot of nonsense!' they'd

13

say if I made too many grand phrases. O perfection! Fortunately, I'm not concerned with it.

Of course, I should not complain if this book succeeded in having a few readers. But I should derive most pleasure from seeing it in the hands of some of those little girls whose faces and persons have the same beauties, the same litheness, as those of my women friends. I often smile kindly at one of these children, either in the street or in houses I frequent. It is at once a retrospective tenderness for the little companions of my childhood, regret at not having a daughter and a longing for a disinterested affection. Never anything perverse, or at least that comes only afterwards. The proof of it is that these little girls generally smile at me too. They see that it is a friend passing by, one who would join happily in their games, if he were not afraid of ridicule and the arrival of their mothers. Even yesterday, at No. 4 Rue du Marché-Saint-Honoré, in the courtyard of a house, I smiled at a charming, dark-haired little girl. Moreover, I often feel, on those evenings when my friends are busy elsewhere, that just two or three of these children could divert me equally well by their vivacity and uninhibited gestures. I should be happy, therefore, if some few of them were to turn the pages of this book as a relaxation from their lessons. Perhaps it may not all be very clear to them, even if it does not escape them completely; though one chapter at least, that in which I tell of my childhood, is certainly designed to amuse them. But the books one reads as a child are never forgotten. The impression they made on us may alter, yet we continue to think of them from time to time. Who knows, indeed, whether they do not give us more than the great books we read later on with either scepticism or envy ? One day, these little girls will remember having read, when they were about thirteen or fourteen, a very odd little book. Perhaps they will seek it out and read it with pleasure once more. They will talk about it to their friends and make their husbands and lovers buy it. I shall then be about fifty and fairly well-known. It will console me for having refrained from putting into it, for the sake of their past innocence, more precise details and more lively scenes.

Chapter 2

*Of all human infirmities, the saddest is the
slumber of the soul.*

PROVERB

I have already mentioned somewhere that place, redolent of tired grace and, on occasion, expensive scent, where, in the early days, I used to go to meet my women friends. I think I have left more of my heart in that rather gloomy spot than anywhere else except for a certain corner of the Folies-Bergère promenade. It was a sort of little restaurant at the top of the Rue Pigalle, not far from the Brasserie Fontaine, and has vanished today. Practically no one went there during the day. There, these women lunched and dined together, in the afternoon awaiting the time to go and dress, and, in the evening, the hour to disperse through the cafés and music-halls as their appointments or caprice dictated.

I lived at that time behind the Panthéon, in an old convent which had been turned into a lodging-house, among a whole crowd of those very distinguished young men from the provinces. Nearly every evening I went out in search of my friends to prepare myself in their company to write this book. Seeking fame all day had, as it were, exhausted my spirit. My room was full of drafts of essays and poems, sometimes too long, sometimes too short, and a number of those admirable books that are so terribly boring. I left it all with a certain relief.

When I arrived, there these women were, idling, dressed up to the nines, occupied, while waiting to go, with clothes, borrowing money, men they had met or were due to meet, spiteful remarks made or to be made, or simply with nothing at all. Elbows on the table or lying back on the benches, a cigarette between lips or fingers, they welcomed me kindly and with a variety of exclamations. We began exchanging gossip or confidences. They consulted me about all kinds of things; each one wanted to have me to herself. Sometimes it was a new dress or a recently bought hat I had to approve: 'Smart, isn't it? Doesn't it look grand!' Sometimes they showed me letters they had received and asked me what they should reply. I did my best to satisfy them, advise them, give them a tip or two, write drafts of their letters for them, indeed pay them a thousand little attentions. They were very grateful to me afterwards in every possible way. Sometimes, one or two of them were missing, having interesting engagements elsewhere, and we entertained ourselves in their absence by adroitly and delicately running them down. If *business* prevented others from going out, I would stay there chatting with them as long as possible, or wander slowly through the streets with them, laughing and talking. We amused ourselves very much.

But more often than not we went to spend the evening in one of the various cafés or in a music-hall. I would sit with them at a table under the lights, or we would mingle with the crowd on the promenade, while they made eyes abundantly and I thought of a thousand things. And, ever and again, one or another of them would leave us to greet an old friend or a fellow-worker. At the end of the evening, if one of them had had no luck, and had a not too-demanding ardour to expend and the price of a cab, I would yield easily enough to her proposals and go home with her. To say that it was always to make love would not be true. But I had, at least, the advantage of going to bed a little earlier than usual.

But the afternoons were often better still. We would agree to meet at one of their houses and I could abandon myself without reserve to the tenderness they inspired in me. What happy times those were! All my childhood's memories were revived. They were all pretty well-known in Paris and, when they told me what ready and intimate complaisancies had gained them their notoriety, I felt as if I had become once more the little boy who in the past had been speechless with admiration at the sight of his mother's lingerie. I told them in detail of that delicious creature of whom they reminded me so continually and in so many ways. My darling mama! Was it not due to her that I loved them as I did? Indeed, I seemed to see something of her in each one of them! They listened to me with a sort of underlying tenderness and excitement, and I knew that their regrets at having no child were to some extent consoled by our chatter and the kisses that followed it. Oh, how the freshness of young girls seemed to me Bon-Marché and Petit-Saint-Thomas beside the Palais de Glace and Café des Princes weariness of these high-class prostitutes! Every facet of their romantic, submissive personalities moved me. The charm of their hair, their black-encircled eyes, their indolent mouths and husky voices, their ready tenderness, the adroitness of their make-up, their often lively gestures and their still more lively speech, and even the hardness they had acquired, all enchanted me. Moreover, it is still much the same today.

And what things they taught me! Did I perhaps add something to it myself, owing to the many memories they awakened in me? All the same, fathers are wrong to tell their sons not to frequent them. In spite of my heedlessness,

18

certain sayings and doings of my women friends have taught me more than many books, in which one never finds what is claimed for them in the blurb: that profound sense of serious things, for instance, which may help one to avoid reading them in future. Do they not practise that horizontal meditation which in the past gave philosophers such admirable results ? At bottom, they are not so stupid as one thinks. Born to make love all their lives, they know how difficult it becomes when things go too far and they avoid falling in love. It is no matter to them whether you utter childish words or passionate obscenities in their arms; there is no reason why they should be carried away too. 'Really' as they have said to me on occasion, 'do you think we're going to exhaust ourselves that much ?' No matter if I make a display of exalted sentiments in their presence when the mood takes me: at most, they think I talk well. At first sight one might suppose they do not understand. It is rather because they have been deceived so often that they view the sublime with suspicion.

Thus I divert myself as often as possible with these creatures for whom tolerance is not merely a word. I, who have so little success with women owing to my shyness and my horror of sentimentality, find in them, when I need them, the women I require. Why did not the five or six charming women I can recall at this very moment, and whom I would have liked to have possessed a few years ago had they not been so chaste, resemble them ? Why lend such importance to so simple and so unromantic an act as making love! We have lost by it no doubt, both they and I, but I have never acquired the patience to do what is known as court a woman.

With my friends, at least, there was no need for that. No need to make fine phrases. A significant glance, a short colloquy, and you go and make love. As if that were not the better way! This was what we did, and I can say that after a month we knew all about each other. Oh, they promised on those first occasions to be wonderfully kind to me, and to do all sorts of things to me: 'You'll see what a good time I'll give you, darling!' etc. How charming they were, trying to excite me, their bodies close to mine, their adorable, worn faces beneath their excessively decorated hats, while I rejoiced my eyes with the contents of their corsage and the undulations of their hips! And I replied: 'Yes, I know all about that! You all say the same, but for a change. . . .' I used to reply like that, slapping them amicably, and then went with them all the same. I had to, indeed, if I wanted to be in their good graces and get from them, later on, things for my book. Besides, that they should more or less impose on me was so unimportant. Indeed, I preferred not to tire myself too much.

Since then, I have hardly done it, not as a regular thing anyway. Matters of love have too little interest for me. To think there are people who steal, kill or commit suicide for the satisfaction of a few seconds! I simply do not understand it, and my friends themselves are inclined to laugh at it. Nevertheless, I am like everyone else. Sometimes, after several weeks of chastity, a month or more on occasion—it depends on the year and whether I'm working or not—I feel a need, 'transports animate me,' as they say in the tragedies, and I take care of them with my friends: 'By the way, couldn't we one afternoon perhaps?' . . . And, of course, we always could, for we are like a married couple now, but I don't know why, or rather I know it all too well, it's rarely satisfactory, and I am always in a bad temper afterwards. It often happens even, though my friends tease me and tell me

I shall make old bones if I go on like that, that I go to bed with one or other of them and do nothing at all; we merely assume a posture together, that's all, legs intertwined, and talk of other people's passions. Delicious moments! Perhaps it's true that there is nothing like platonic love? And then, even if I were capable of it, I would have certain scruples in enjoying their charming favours too often. In the first place they are busy enough with all the gentlemen they take home with them without, more often than not, knowing them any better than in Gavarni's cartoon: 'Darling, tell me, what's your Christian name?' And, besides, it was all right in the old days when they treated me like the others. But now it would be indelicate, and everyone would feel it to be so. Indeed, it would be all the more so because they make so little in spite of all the trouble they take and the good they do. Oh, one has to admit that men are mean! When one thinks that these women, who should be kept in luxury, more often than not have little more than the strict necessities of life, and then only by getting into debt! At moments it makes me feel quite depressed. We could be so happy, if things were better!

Above all, it is not so funny to think that all these sessions, of two or three, lasting an hour or a night (in which they do more or less, according to what you give them or what you look like) exhaust them a little more each day, particularly the more satisfactory occasions. I sometimes even feel a certain melancholy at seeing them fading away almost before my eyes. 'To think that one day they'll be old and even look like concierges!' I think sometimes. And yet, I should be lying if I spoke only of my regret. For is not this very fatigue of love, that glazes and encircles their eyes and hardens their faces a little, the most exciting part of their beauty? When I see them rather done up, as they say, on the morrow of a night of serious love-making, a little defiled as it were, I savour emotionally their sad and signal weariness. Others may love youth! I do not know whether these women would have the same attraction for me if they had the freshness of young girls of good family.

Chapter 3

'Lord! What a horrid child!'

MY MOTHER

I do not know whether the reader will be much amused by my reminiscences of childhood. I have been wondering for the last five years at least whether I should write them and I have decided to do so only now! Besides, who knows whether the child I was, and whom I now see again with a precision that is almost uncanny, will not reproach me, when I have done, with having gone too far in this book, in so far as it concerns him. Poor little dear! As my friends so tenderly say when I talk to them about him. Anyway, perhaps he will make a few good pages.

You can laugh at me if you like: but I feel rather moved on approaching the subject of this little boy. I even wonder whether I shall not become outrageously maudlin in writing of him. After the moderation I have displayed on the subject of those women, it would be a trifle exaggerated. But no, I shall write of him as I have written of them, with the same suave gentleness and a similar care not to shock. As to that, indeed, how easily I could do the opposite! But I would not want to distress him by showing him less loyalty than I have those women he already loved. Little, vanished figure, smiling at me out of the distant past! Would I not also be lying to myself from the very depths of the years, if I sought to flatter him or make of him an object of compassion? Besides, my dearest wish is that he should be liked through the medium of these pages as he then was and as, in his

23

heart of hearts, he wanted to be loved. No, I shall say nothing about the child that is not true. But if, here and there, I unconsciously give way to too much emotion, consider, by way of excuse for me, that the little boy I once was has no one here below to adorn his memory and record his early bent towards tenderness and reverie but myself.

My whole childhood was spent in that district of Paris which lies between the Butte Montmartre and the great boulevards, bordered on one side by the Rue de Clichy and the Chaussée d'Antin, and on the other by the Rue Rochechouart and the Faubourg Montmartre. I was sometimes taken, of course, to the Tuileries and the Champs-Elysées, and I often visited the Théâtre-Français backstage. But these were great expeditions, which did not divert me very much, in particular the Comédie, where I used to go with my father, and where the masterpieces of the contemporary theatre were already inclined to send me to sleep. The one memory I have retained is that of the fifth act of the *Mariage de Figaro*, the act in the garden, when Cherubin goes by humming his ballad. The garden seemed to me huge and the ballad made me cry: '*J'avais une marraine. . . .*' No, the more I think of them, the more I realise they were not my favourite outings. The district most familiar to me, in which my eyes were filled with scenes I was to recollect for ever, was that which lies between the Rue Notre-Dame-de-Lorette and the Rue Fontaine, the Boulevard de Clichy and the Boulevard Rochechouart, and the Rue Rochechouart and the Rue Lamartine.

The whole of this district has remained for me full of a peculiar life and colour of its own. Born a few streets lower down, towards the Palais-Royal, it is there I grew up, after

24

having been so ill that the doctors said I could not live; it was there I walked so often, stared at so much, and began to love women, a slow little boy who rarely smiled despite his happiness. The houses in which my father lived, in the Rue des Martyrs and the Rue Rodier, the house in which my old nurse, Marie, lived in the Rue Clauzel, and the houses where I went to visit ladies whom my father knew, in the Rue de la Tour-d'Auvergne, the Avenue Trudaine and the Boulevard des Batignolles, have not altered since that time. Whenever I pass that way and come to the corner in the Faubourg Montmartre where there is a jeweller's shop on the right with a huge clock with a double face, I am always moved to find the district pretty much the same as when I knew it. And when, higher up, I stop at the doors of the houses to gaze into the courtyards I have crossed so often, either alone or held by the hand, I am assailed by a tender, an indescribable nostalgia as I see myself as I then was, not very tall for my age, my large head inclined a little to one side and with eyes everyone admired.

Indeed, there is not a street in the whole district that is not full of a sort of friendly feeling. I have played with a troop of charming little girls for whole afternoons at the top of the Rue Milton, which at that time was lined on both sides with empty sites behind wooden hoardings. For years, I accompanied my father each morning to his hairdresser in the Rue Lamartine, at the corner of Rue Rochechouart. We used to go down the Rue Rodier, the lower part of the Rue de Maubeuge, then turn into the Rue Lamartine. I can still smell the mist that lay over those mornings and the mingled odours coming from the market in the Rue Cadet, and I see again Bérard's barber's shop with its judas in the ceiling.

For years, too, I went each evening from my father's house to the Rue Clauzel, accompanied by my old nurse, Marie, in whose house I slept. The dairy-shop in the Rue de la Tour-d'Auvergne, into which she went one evening, leaving me to walk on, so that I thought I had lost her and began crying, still exists; and the coal-merchant's, where she bought her coal each evening for the next day, is in the same place at the entrance to the Rue Clauzel.

I used to go to the Protestant infants' school in the Rue Milton, where I fell down one day and got a huge bump on my forehead. I remember the headmaster, M. Lesur, very well, a charming man, and the master of my class, a certain Léonardo, who was not charming at all, and had a habit of beating us on the hands with a ruler. I was also at the communal school in the Impasse Rodier, which must have been transferred elsewhere, for I can no longer find it. I played truant from it once for a fortnight, telling my father there were no classes, either because the headmaster's mother had died, or because the master was ill, etc. At that time, we lived at 21, Rue des Martyrs. My father believed me, and I was able to lounge about the streets all day. But one day, at lunch-time, someone came from the school to find out why I was absent. What a beating I got in the little salon beside the dining-room! I can still hear myself screaming to my father, who was practically trampling me underfoot with rage: 'I'm sorry, Father, I'll never do it again!' But he went on beating me just the same.

I also sometimes played in the market of the Rue Hippolyte-Lebas, with my friends, the Langlois, two brothers, sons of a baker in the Rue des Martyrs. I used often to walk alone through the long passage, vanished today, that led from the Rue Rodier to the Rue Maubeuge. I remember the old-clothes woman whom we knew in the Rue Lamartine, at the corner of the Rue Milton, beside a caged-bird merchant. I remember, too, in the Rue Lamartine, the house in which one of my father's mistresses lived. One day she shot herself and we went to see her at Lariboisière, or at Beaujon. All these memories are still so alive to me that, in spite of the sense I have since acquired, I can never cross the Place Saint-Georges without stopping and gazing with emotion at the fountain in which I used to sail a little boat.

How much else there was to hold my attention, certain shops for instance, of which barely a dozen have changed their location, and certain houses and the impression they made on me which I remember so well. The colour-merchant in the Rue des Martyrs with his striped shop-front; the laundry with its tin sign; the little general store at the corner of the Rue Hippolyte-Lebas (the Rue Haute-Lebas as women new to the district said, because of the abbreviation on the name plate); the big block of flats opposite No. 19; M. Randon's books and book-shop, and the old clothes-merchant with all her furbelows. In the Rue Clauzel, the girls' school, and an artist's house with a decorated façade; the low house in the Rue de Steinkerque, where my old nurse used often to take me to visit an old lady; and the house in the Rue Rodier, opposite ours, where women with powdered faces sang all day. Oh, those women, I hear them still! They must have been singing a popular song, such as the *Valse bleue* or *Froufrou* are today. I cannot remember what it was called, but I do remember that considering my age, it induced an extraordinary melancholy in me. I could even write the tune down if I knew anything of music; and it had these words, the only ones I remember:

Le rossignol, mignonne   ⎫
N'a pas encor chanté   ⎬bis
  Brune Joli-ie   ⎭
  O mon ami-ie
  O mon-on amie
Ce n'est pas l'heure des adieux. . . .

Practically none of all this has changed. This district of
Paris is one of the few that has not been rebuilt, probably
because of its steep slopes. There are neither bicycles nor
motor-cars to be seen there. It still has something of Gavarni's Breda Street, of the little Italian streets of Louis
Lurine, full of artists and prostitutes, a few yards away from
the noisy Faubourg Montmartre. Yes, indeed, little of all
this has changed. It is merely several years older.

The Butte Montmartre was still just a steep, open space,
without all the steps and ugliness of today; I often went there
to walk with my nurse, as if in the open country. I remember
what delightful places I thought the Passage Verdeau, the
Passage Jouffroy and the Passage de l'Opéra, with the bright
reflections from their shops, particularly the third with its
big toy-shop, where I always coveted a mechanical horse.
The Faubourg Montmartre seemed to me a huge place,
busy and crowded. I was much taken with the shops there,
such as Le Cardinal Fesch, La Ville de Londres and Godchau. But Godchau interested me particularly. At the door
stood an employee and a lay-figure who looked exactly alike.
I could never tell which was which.

I recall, as if I had left them but yesterday, my father's
various flats, that at 13, Rue des Martyrs, with the big salon
in which rehearsals took place, that in the Rue Rodier with
the balcony on which, for a time, we kept a rabbit brought

28

back from the Bois de Boulogne, and that, again in the Rue des Martyrs, at No. 21, where, on reaching the age of ten, I first had a room of my own. I recollect standing at the window of an actress of the Comédie-Française, Mme Jouassaint, at 14, Rue Notre-Dame-de-Lorette, a house which communicated with our own—on the first floor, the first window on the left, as you look at the house—to see Thiers's funeral go by. I remember also the Fayolle children, who lived in the flat opposite ours on the same storey, at 13, Rue des Martyrs, and with whom I used to play in a big room at the back. I met one of them a few years ago in the house-surgeon's room at the Hôtel-Dieu. The other, grown into a pretty woman, is now playing small parts at the Comédie-Française under the name of Faylis. One night at the theatre, in February 1901, when standing by the door leading on to the stage, talking to a friend, I found myself beside Mlle Faylis, who was waiting to go on-stage. 'It's a long time since I've seen you, Mademoiselle,' the friend I was with remarked by way of greeting. 'And I haven't seen Mademoiselle for even longer than you!' I said to my friend. Mlle Faylis could not make out what it was all about. By then, I was going to the theatre only very rarely and she had no idea who I was. I told her, reminding her of the flat, of our games and of the little boy I once had been. She remembered me and smiled with a youthful charm, her eyes bright, and her face made-up beneath the dead hair of her wig. I recollected that charming passage in *Aimienne*, by my dear Jean de Tinan, the lines at the bottom of page thirty-six and at the top of page thirty-seven.

And how many more memories I have!

One Shrove Tuesday, I nearly died of fear at the masks. I was five years old. My old nurse, Marie, had thought to amuse

me by taking me to see them. She had to carry me hastily
home in her arms. I had a temperature all night, and refused
to go out for several days, afraid of seeing the masks again.
Alas, since then I have become somewhat hardened: I can
now walk quite happily through the streets in spite of the
grotesque appearance of the military and the spectacle of
so many ugly people.

I recollect very well, when I went to find my father in the
café, the pleasure I took, while waiting for him, in the little
pictures which then still appeared on the cover of the *Vie
Parisienne*. I have, too, preserved a lively taste for certain
paintings of the period between 1860 and 1880. I remember
my dog Tabac, who accompanied me everywhere, fetching
me from school and allowing no one to come near me, even
to give me a kiss; my big wooden horse, whose tail I plaited;
the Faisan Doré Restaurant, in the Rue des Martyrs, with
its little white and gold room, which was so brightly lit at
night; the sort of market at the corner of the Rue Notre-
Dame-de-Lorette and the Rue La Rochefoucauld, burnt
down a few years ago; the little tap with Eau-de-Cologne in
the Passage Verdeau; the big entrance in the Rue de Châteaudun, opposite the Trinité, behind which was a mirror;
the baths, also in the Rue de Châteaudun, to which I once
accompanied my mother, who made me wait opposite in a
fine courtyard with two entrances; the Place du Carrousel,
with a fair and a captive balloon; the Square of the Trinité,
the Square Montholon and the Square Rollin, where my old
nurse used to take me to play; the railway which an actor in
my father's company was always promising me; and my godmother Bianca, then at the Comédie-Française, whom I
often used to go and see at her house in the Rue de Rome.
On her chimney-piece was a sort of doll with two faces,

Jean qui pleure et Jean qui rit, which filled me with wonder. One day she gave me a big theatre which I carried about with me everywhere, even out-of-doors, to amuse my friends.

I remember the snowy winter of 1879, and the white slope of the Rue des Martyrs in the mornings; Mme Favrier, so fair and scented, who lived in the Boulevard de Clichy, I think; the Punch and Judy show on the Champs-Elysées, where one day I attended every performance; the dance-hall of the Elysée-Montmartre, where I was sometimes taken in the evenings to amuse me; the Fernando circus where, so it seems, there was a clown who fascinated me; Robert Houdin, on one occasion, and Victor Hugo, on a night when *Hernani* was being played, behind the scenes at the Comédie, beside the property man's little room, which has since disappeared. My father introduced me to him, and he stroked my cheek, rather amused by my father's telling him that I always wanted to be given Hernani's sword, which I believed to be really broken. What charming and delightful things I could recount if I gave way to the flow of memory! But, be still, my heart! We must not overdo childhood's memories; we can use them later, if the women have not wearied us too much.

I grew up in this district, therefore, mostly under the influence of women, with more often than not for sole company my old nurse Marie, my dear mother Pezé, as I called her, who had brought me up. As I write, I have before me two photographs taken at Pierre Petit's so that they might be sent to my mother. The first shows the dear old thing in her Sunday best, with her string bonnet and silk fichu, myself beside her, shy and dreamy, one hand placed on her shoulder and holding, in the other, a little bowler-hat, which is really rather sweet. The second is of

31

me alone, taken the same day and looking rather more posed. At bottom, I have changed so little that it seems to me, as I look at these photographs, that it was only yesterday I went to Pierre Petit's with my old nurse, and I believe, if I became a child again and returned there with her, I should pose in exactly the same way. We took Tabac so that he might pose with us, but he refused to keep still and we had to give up the idea. I can still see the big room in which Pierre Petit worked, the sort of dais on which he placed us, and the camera at the further end of the studio. I posed with Marie first, then alone. . . . Oh, that little boy, that little boy, where is he now, and with what tenderness I look back on him! Could I but live those distant days once more, could I become that child again! I had no ambitions, no literary preoccupations. I knew nothing of the urge to write and the boredom of making fair copies; I had a sort of melancholy which was enough for my happiness, and my head, as I held it inclined to one side, was full only of delightful and frivolous things.

I was already far from turbulent. The least thing could amuse me. You would never have found me playing at soldiers, and military bands, marching troops and so on excited my attention no more than they do today. I could sit happily on a chair for hours together, or hidden under an old jeweller's bench we had in the house, without uttering a word and without feeling bored. On several occasions at this time even my father became anxious and went out into the street to fetch in children to try to make me play. My big wooden horse and a few pictures sufficed me for toys. When someone called, I fled. I remember that once they tried to make me sing; eventually I brought myself to do so but only after hiding for some time behind an open door. The other boys, into whose company my father forced me and to whom I lent my theatre, rather frightened me, and indeed I never knew how to play at marbles nor at ball nor at any other game. My greatest pleasures were of a quieter sort. Sometimes, I used to go, as I have said—I enjoy writing of these things so much that I could go on forever—to make sand-castles in the Square Montholon, the Square de la Trinité or the Square Rollin, or wander through the Passages, like the Passage Verdeau, the Passage Jouffroy or the Passage de l'Opéra, in company with my dear mother Pezé, or, again, go to sit with her in the open-air on the heights of the Butte. Sometimes, too, I would go out and wander about the district alone, quite the little man. I would make a big circle by the Rue Clauzel, the Rue Bréda, the Rue Frochot, the Boulevard de Clichy, the Rue Fontaine, the Rue Notre-Dame-de-Lorette, walking slowly and happily, enjoying everything, the movement in the streets and the displays in the shop-windows, stopping ever and again to gaze in at some window where, at once concealed and yet visible behind the shutters, a woman in a bright dressing-gown would bow her head and smile. Or, again, I would go and find my little friends at the top of the Rue Milton; they were so graceful, so docile, so pretty even and their company delighted me. How delicious it was to be with them! My father laughingly called them my mistresses. 'Here's a penny,' he would say sometimes when he was in a good humour, 'go and sleep with your women.' I can still remember one of them, whose parents kept a baker's shop at the corner of the Boulevard de Clichy and the Rue Fromentin. I obeyed her exactly as if she were a grown-up, so subject was I to the charm of her manner, and I often waited for her, concealed at the corner of the Rue Fromentin, when she went home to meals. Oh, how readily

I would hand over Alsace and Lorraine all over again to recover those pleasures! I always had a few pennies on me with which to buy these girls skipping-ropes, thus learning early how expensive women are; and I had to do it again and again. They used to skip before me as if wishing to give me pleasure, while I watched them in silence, leaning against a wall, or sitting on the edge of the pavement. I was already attracted by the charm of their faces. It did not occur to me that they might well be laughing at me for buying them skipping-ropes from which they alone benefited. For I was content with their evident pleasure and the little laughing kisses they gave me. 'Alas for the heart's simplicity! So soon destroyed,' as Théophile Gautier has said somewhere.

As I mentioned above, I did not sleep at my father's house but at my nurse's in the Rue Clauzel. There were two reasons for this: in the first place, I was frightened at night and could not be left alone, and then my father so rarely came home by himself. . . . How clearly I can see the little attic room Marie occupied on the sixth floor of the big house bearing the number 14 to which we returned every evening at about half past nine. I always wanted her to carry me upstairs; indeed, I always wanted to be carried everywhere. When I went out with my father, I had to make my legs work, and march along rather in the ridiculous way soldiers do; but, with Marie, I had only to ask to be carried two or three times and she could never refuse me. On reaching the fifth floor, she turned into a little, dark passage that led to a small curving staircase of no more than ten steps leading up to the sixth storey. The door of her room was immediately opposite. How happy I was in that room, and what quiet hours I spent there, much happier hours than in my father's flat! Everything about it delighted me, from my little arm-

34

chair and my child's table to the big bed and the old chest-of-drawers, whose brass handles I can still hear falling back into place with a little echo. I remember that room so well that, if I wished, I could draw a plan of it here, showing the position of every piece of furniture.

At the bottom of the Rue des Martyrs, on the right, there is a money-changer's booth, which was not of the same colour then as it is today, and I spent many hours in front of it at the period of which I am writing. Since my father had to be at the theatre every evening at eight o'clock, we dined at six. After dinner, he would take me on his knees for a little and pet me, before going off. I would then, weather permitting, go out and take a turn in the district till it was time to return to the Rue Clauzel with Marie. The lights had all been lit. It was as if one could hear invisible orchestras in the distance; and the women whom I had seen in the afternoon walking about in négligé were now dressed up to the nines and hurrying towards the boulevards and places where one 'works'. I walked slowly down the Rue des Martyrs on the left-hand pavement, casting a sympathetic glance at the little white and gold room of the Faisan Doré, stopping sometimes at the botton of the street at old Salomon's jeweller's shop, beside the colour-merchant's, and sometimes I went for a little while to look at the trace-horses at the entrance to the Rue Notre-Dame-de-Lorette. Then I crossed the street and went and stood in front of the money-changer's window, staying there sometimes, utterly absorbed, for over an hour. What an extraordinary thing! I can recover the sensation of those evenings spent before that window full of old coins, out-of-date notes, assignats, etc. Yes, sitting in my chair writing these interesting memoirs—and they are, aren't they?—it seems to me that, if I so wished, I could once again become that little boy standing in front of the booth, and I can feel the movement of people passing behind me, and on my face is the warmth of the gas-lights in the window. . . . But I was pretty contemptuous of the display within the shop window. 'You can think what you like,' as a popular tune has it, but a few bare-headed women who were accosting male passers-by interested me a great deal more, and the money-changer's window was but a pretext to stand there and watch them. Unfortunately, I did not really understand their manoeuvres. I saw them accosting gentlemen in a confidential sort of way, but I had no idea what they could be saying to them. I thought it must be something polite, but since I could never manage to overhear, I remained uncertain. When one of them succeeded in detaining a passer-by and, after a few words, they went off together into the Rue Lamartine or the Rue des Martyrs, I felt a certain pleasure that one of them at least had not been rebuffed. But when, after a while, I saw her return alone and begin all over again, I failed to understand. I wondered what she had done with the man and why, when she had seemed to be getting on well with him, she had left him so soon in order to seek another. I asked myself these questions every evening as I returned home, and I could never find the answers; indeed, I found them only many years later. Furthermore, you can see as well as I that Gautier's exclamation, which I quoted above, might perhaps have been more appropriate here.

Sometimes, I went to watch other women at work higher up, at the corner of the Rue de Morée (today the Rue Manuel) and the Rue des Martyrs. One of them, a little on the old side and wearing a sort of bonnet, inspired me with both interest and curiosity. At first, she seemed to me to look exactly like a wet-nurse, like those I met in the squares. 'And yet,' I said to myself, 'the others always have a baby in their arms!' And I wondered why this one wandered about like that in the street, with her bonnet rather askew, it seemed to me, and without a baby. Indeed, this wet-nurse without a baby in her arms seemed to me very peculiar.

But all these pleasures were as nothing compared to those Loulou gave me. She was a lady living on the fourth floor of Marie's house; she was very kind to me and I had given her the name of Loulou in my baby language. When we got home, Marie sometimes looked into her room to gossip a moment, while I went to sleep on her lap, only later to find myself undressed and in bed without having been conscious of the process. But, more often than not, we met her at the corner of the Rue Clauzel and the Rue des Martyrs. Indeed, we met her there nearly every evening as we passed by. She appeared to be walking up and down with a calm yet alert air. From however far away I caught sight of her, I always wanted to run to her. 'Loulou! Loulou!' I cried; 'I want to give Loulou a kiss!' And for all that Marie tried to hold me back and Loulou pretended not to hear me, in the end Marie always had to let go of my hand and Loulou stop that I might kiss her. . . . I need close my eyes only for a moment to see Loulou as she then was, dressed in the fashion of the period, her black silk cape trimmed with braid, her draped skirt furnished with a bustle, and her felt hat surrounded by a velvet band. She seemed always rather pale to me, her eyes too bright, and her lips too red. She would lean down towards me, rather shyly it seemed, or raise me gently in her arms to kiss me and, when our faces touched, I felt a little intoxicated by the scent she wore. Marie would then take me

37

by the hand again and lead me away, scolding a little. I would turn two or three times as we went on to look back at Loulou who had begun walking up and down once more with the same light step. 'Why does she walk up and down like that?' I wondered. 'Somebody must be keeping her waiting.'

It was but a few years ago that I learned from my Aunt Fanny what Loulou was doing every evening at the corner of the Rue Clauzel and why my nurse wished to prevent my going to kiss her. This aunt, being on her way through Paris, had come to see me at my father's. One evening, she was accompanying Marie and me to the Rue Clauzel and, when we reached the corner and saw Loulou, I immediately wanted to run to kiss her as usual. Seeing Marie trying to restrain me as best she could, my aunt said: 'Why don't you want him to say good evening to the lady? It shows he's an affectionate child.' 'But she's a street-walker,' my old nurse replied, 'so you understand. . . .' My aunt was much amused.

Mme Leroux, moreover, was the only one of her sort among the ladies I knew. Those who came to the house or to whose houses I went glittered in another way. They were little actresses, or the mistresses of friends of my father, or my father's mistresses, for he was very much of a ladies' man. I spent my time being kissed by them, sitting on their laps and hiding my face as much as possible in their bosoms. I should find it very difficult to say now what precise pleasure I derived from this; but, undoubtedly, when I allowed myself to be petted by all these young ladies, I was preparing myself as best I could for my friends of today. I remember one of them very well, Mlle Alice Chaine, who lived in the Rue Rodier, I think in that very house opposite ours where the lodgers were always singing. She was very friendly towards me, not at all stuck-up and I was never embarrassed by her. She always wore a dressing-gown and it was invariably half unbuttoned. Her pretty fair face and her masses of lace delighted me so much that I would have given her whole treasures if I had possessed any. It was as if I had already grasped the fact that women are unlikely to love one unless one gives them something. Having no treasures, I gave this young woman a number of pebbles I kept in reserve. 'Here, Alice,' I would say to her, 'here's some money. I'm keeping you. When you have none left, you can come and ask me for more.'

It was thus I kept this adorable creature on the cheap. She never put on airs with me, loaded me with cakes and kisses, and had the great merit of not boring me too much. How unfettered would have been the love between this charming woman and myself had we met again a few years later, when I was eighteen for instance. A lost happiness better not contemplated, unless it be with a smile. Since then, things have changed a good deal, and I am not sure I do not give more than I receive. My women friends keep cigarettes for me and will give me the rest too, if I want it, but I know from experience that all the pebbles in the world would not content them. Even with little girls I no longer have the advantages I had then. Is it because I have lost some of my ingenuousness? But I suspect, if I tried to play nicely with them now, it would cost me more dear than all the skipping-ropes I used to buy my little friends, though they could use up a lot of them. Nevertheless, I do not despair. I tell myself that times such as those of my child-hood will perhaps return one day. I see myself being loved once again by compliant and generous young persons, or at least by one, and this time sumptuously. What a lark that would be!

A few years later, towards the middle of the year 1881, my mother, whom I hardly knew, came to spend a few days in Paris, both to amuse herself a little and catch a glimpse of her son. We were then living at 21, Rue des Martyrs, in a maisonette on the far side of the courtyard, and it was there that I began to learn the trials of life. My old nurse Marie had left the house; and a young woman of a quite different type had taken her place. I now had a room in my father's house, a little low-ceilinged room, into which I was shut every night immediately after dinner. It was the end of my fun. . . .

My mother arrived one afternoon. She was staying in furnished lodgings, which still exist, in the Passage Laferrière, No. 16, I think, and she wanted at once to see what I looked like. Our meeting was brief. After a few minutes, during which I remained dumb, hardly daring to look at her and calling her shyly 'Madame', she rose to her feet, smoothed her skirts, made up her face and went out. It was arranged that I should go and see her the next morning and spend the whole day with her, and that she would bring me back in the evening to the Brasserie des Martyrs—at the corner of the Rue des Martyrs and of the Rue Hippolyte-Lebas; it no longer exists—where my father always called in on his way home from the theatre.

Next morning, therefore, I went off to see her in that house in the Passage Laferrière and, shy as I was, it was certainly no paltry event for me. The Passage Laferrière has since become the Rue Laferrière and the two gates which shut it off at each end, at the Rue Notre-Dame-de-Lorette and at the Rue Bréda, have disappeared; but, that apart, the whole locality is still as it was then, quiet and feminine. I no longer remember what name I asked for when I arrived in order to be shown my mother's room; or rather, I hover between two names I have known her use, without being quite certain which it was at that period. However that may be, her room was pointed out to me; as far as I can remember, it was on the first floor; and when I had knocked and she had opened to me, or having opened the door by turning the key which was in the lock—I cannot remember that either—I entered the room where this woman who was so important to my life was staying. I found her still in bed, sitting up a little, her hair rather untidy, her naked arms outside the bed-clothes, and her bosom rather naked, too, because her nightdress had slipped down. . . . She told me to come to her so she might kiss me, and I went over to the bed, at once happy and embarrassed. She took my head in her hands, drew it down to her breast, and kissed me quickly like a child. I felt the softness of her breasts under my cheek as they quivered in time to her kisses. I marvelled silently at her elegant, fashionable lingerie, thrown so negligently over every chair in the room, while the scent that came from it gradually made me feel dizzy as did that of my grown-up friends. It all smacked of frivolity, coquetry and the superficialities of love. After a moment spent thus, she got up, cleared a chair for me to sit down, washed and dressed in my presence, going quickly and familiarly to and fro; and I could not take my eyes off her. Oh, what a pretty mama she was, I assure you, gay, graceful and vivacious! It was the first time I had ever seen a woman in such intimacy and I probably did not appreciate the moment to the full. Yet I remember my regret on leaving that room in which I had seen my mother in bed and in which she had clasped me so closely in her arms. . . . What a frivolous grace was hers as she got up! I would give a lot to recover that moment.

I seem to remember that we went to luncheon with my father, but I cannot be sure of it. And yet, the vision I have of that luncheon in our little dining-room in the Rue des Martyrs, with my father on one side, myself in the middle, and my mother on the other, for the first and last time, seems familiar to me. But how long ago it is! And though I have an astonishing memory, certain details sometimes escape me. Immediately after luncheon, the treats began. First we went to the Jardin d'Acclimatation in a cab. It must have been my first visit. I went for a ride on one of those ponies led by a keeper, saw all the animals, etc. It all seemed very far from the Rue des Martyrs and my fountains in the Place Saint-Georges and the Place Pigalle. Now that I come to think of it, it was a happy age when beasts still interested me! I have seen so many since and been so bored by them! Then we returned in a cab along the Avenue des Champs-Elysées and the Rue de Rivoli, as far as a restaurant at the Palais-Royal, Véfour, I have recently ascertained, where we dined. All my life I shall be able to summon up the vision of myself at that restaurant table by a window, close to other diners, who stared at us, my mother sitting opposite me, and the garden, down below on the right, within my field of vision. I must have had just that particular aura of the cocotte's child out on a party with his mother which I have sometimes seen since surrounding other children!

Then we went to the Châtelet, where the first performances of *Michel Strogoff* were being given. I remember little about the performance. We left somewhat before the end, I seem to remember, and took another cab. As I have already said, my mother was to take me to my father at the Brasserie des Martyrs at the corner of the Rue Hippolyte-Lebas. But, when we arrived in the Faubourg Montmartre, the cabby turned suddenly to the right and, at the end of a little street, stopped before a brightly lit entrance, by which people were going in and out, the stir they made being like gusts of music. It was the Folies-Bergère, which I probably did not as yet know. Having dismissed the cab we went in. The few minutes I spent there that night have left a memory no less vivid than my visits to the Passage Laferrière in the morning and the dinner I have just mentioned at the Palais-Royal.

That night, holding my mother's hand, I entered the Folies-Bergère for the first time. It is all still much the same as it then was, particularly that part of it with which I am concerned. She had probably come to meet friends, for we hurried through the foyer to the promenade round the performance hall. Oh, that place on the promenade, where I stood that night for an hour while my mother chatted with her friends, is still far from lacking in interest for me today. When I go to the Folies-Bergère, I nearly always go to that very place, waiting for my friends to let me know, by a word or a sign in passing, whether I am to go away or wait for them so that we can go elsewhere together. It is immediately to the right of the entrance, in a sort of corner made by the wall, precisely opposite the sixth pillar, counting from the right as you face them. It is not a particularly comfortable spot, for there are no seats and the people walking to and fro are inclined to jostle you continually. But I lived a moment in my mother's company on that very spot, and the clear memory I have of myself as I

43

then was often inclines me to prefer it to any other. Everything I saw delighted me, and changed me a little too. I knew many similar places already. I had been to the Boule-Noire, for instance, to the Elysée-Montmartre and to the Comédie-Française; lights and evening-dresses were no novelty to me. But what I saw now seemed to have a brilliance all its own, an added vividness, a greater splendour and a greater harmony, and the women, too, seemed more beautiful than those of the Boule-Noire and the Elysée-Montmartre, who were often rather common, or those of the Comédie, who were always so affected. I was also fascinated by my mother. She had her back half-turned to me, and I dared stare at her at last while she talked. I rediscovered that frivolous air of hers I had noticed in the morning; I listened to her continual laughter and her clear, lively voice; my eyes missed none of her supple movements. How very much at ease she seemed amid these lights, amid all this bustle! I was amazed, too, by all the people she knew. Passers-by, both ladies and gentlemen, were continually coming up to greet her with that particular warmth one reserves for someone not seen for a long time. Oh, she must have been much loved if one were to judge by the warmth of those greetings! From time to time, she turned to me, pointing me out. 'Ah, your son! . . . How charming he is! . . .' And they patted my cheek as if I were a friend. Delicious moments, whose rather feverish atmosphere I shall never forget. And over it all was the sound of music— muted, sonorous, rising, falling, its rhythm catchy, lively, deafening, even crazy—rising from the orchestra in the hall. No doubt it was merely some popular tune, such as *Le Petit Vin de Bordeaux*, or *L'Amant d'Amanda*, or *La Valse des Roses*, which everyone was humming at the time.

44

Closing-time came at last, and my mother and I left with a group of people. We went to supper in a neighbouring tavern, then set out up the Faubourg Montmartre and the Rue des Martyrs, talking all the time. My mother handed me over to my father, who was waiting for me at his brasserie. She kissed me, I seem to remember, and left. I saw her again only once or twice, two or three years later, and but for half an hour on each occasion. For the last twenty years, I have heard nothing of her, except that she is married.

I have recently revisited the Rue des Martyrs district of which I have talked perhaps too much. So much the worse! I wanted to check my memories before embarking on this chapter. I wandered through each one of those streets, familiar to me as much from my childhood's walks as, later on, from the innumerable times I waited vainly in them for my women friends in the early days of our acquaintance. The memories I have tried to evoke became more vivid at every step I took. I was continually being brought to a halt by some street corner being the same as ever or by some house I knew well. There were shop-keepers I recognised. I stared at them and they stared back, trying to remember where they had seen me before. Even the air I breathed was familiar; every single thing gave me the illusion of having become a child again. In the Rue Manuel, I even saw the woman in the bonnet whom I used to take for a wet-nurse. These twenty years, in which I have become more serious-minded, have left her as wanton as she was when I used to go and watch her. 'Come along, deary, have some fun!' she murmured as I passed her. And, at these words, I felt as shy as the little boy she used to fascinate in the past. I made a point, too, of going to the Rue Laferrière, where the memory of my mother hovers for me for ever. Almost unconsciously,

45

I found myself walking down it as slowly as I had on that distant morning, so sweet to my memory, when, awed and thoughtful, I went to see her. I looked at the house, at the window of the room in which I had first seen her looking so pretty and so elegant. If I had dared, I would have gone in and asked permission to sit in that room for an hour or so, to dream nostalgically of that unforgettable creature. The things that happened to me in it have affected me so profoundly that I am sure nothing can have effaced them. Then I went to the Rue Clauzel to see the house Marie had lived in. I asked the concierge if Mme Leroux still lived there, and Mlle Legrain, whom my nurse had also known. The first had left long ago and I was able only to see the second, now very old, who was living in a small room on the fifth floor. I excused myself for disturbing her, and told her that, from literary nostalgia, I was in search of memories. She remembered very well my dear mother Pezé, with her rush basket, and the shy thoughtful little boy who followed her about everywhere. 'It's a long time ago,' she said in a voice I could scarcely hear. 'And now you're a man!' And, thinking how little of a man I had been a few moments before, I tried to assume a casual note on which to bid her goodbye. Then I went into the little passage that leads to the staircase by which Marie and I used to reach our room. Nothing had changed; even the tiled floor had not been repaired; the ceiling had merely become much lower and I should now have had to stoop to climb the little staircase. I went down to the fourth floor and knocked at the door of the room in which Mme Leroux used to live. In any event, I wanted once again to see that room which the first of my friends, that poor light-of-love, had inhabited. A young woman dressed in a sort of négligé, opened the door. I

46

asked for Mme Leroux and showed feigned astonishment when she said she did not know her. 'Perhaps she's the lodger I've replaced?' she said. And, as I started explaining, she invited me in. But I hardly knew where to begin. Everything in the room aimed at being coquettish, everything was a little loud, and the lodger herself seemed far from austere. At length, I began talking. I told her how many times I had gone up and down those stairs long ago etc. The far from austere young woman understood at once. 'Childhood memories, aren't they? One always goes back to them, doesn't one?' and so on. To tell the truth, I was not listening to her. I was concerned only with the little boy who had once sat where I was sitting now. I was thinking only of him. I could see him again, alone behind a door or hidden under a piece of furniture. I felt once again how dear he was to me, with his deep eyes, the curve of his mouth, his half-smile and his dreamy, gentle expression. It seemed to me, too, that it was Loulou who was standing there, ready to kiss me as much as I wished, Loulou. . . . And such a nostalgia for the past seized on me that I nearly broke down. Luckily, the conversation took another, a contemporary turn. The young woman talked and I saw that she was far from wrong when she said that she had replaced Mme Leroux. She replaced her very well indeed. . . . What do you expect! These emotions had put my nerves on edge; while, on her side, the young woman went on becoming less and less austere. I was thinking more and more of Loulou, whom I should have liked so much to see again, and then. . . . Oh, short and cheap though it was, it seemed to me that it was Loulou who held me in her arms, as in the past, who kissed me—for this young woman kissed, which is rare, so it seems, among her kind—and I should have liked to stay

47

there for hours rehearsing my memories! But everything has an end. I had to go. Relieved of a small sum, I left it all, the house, Mlle Legrain and the prostitute, leaning against the wall as I went downstairs, a prey to a ridiculous emotion, if you like to look on it thus, but which, if I listened to my heart, would seize on me again today. . . .

To think that I have so often gone in by the *porte cochère* of that house in the Rue Clauzel, that I have gone up and down those stairs so many times, that I have slept so many nights in that little room, and that there remains nothing at all of those happy days but a few pages I shall take a dislike to tomorrow. To think that my old Marie, who was so kind to me, has for long been no more than an anonymous dust, scattered I know not where, and that I was never able to tell her, since I became a man, of the memories I have of her. To think that my little friends of the Rue Milton are today perhaps wives or prostitutes and that, if we passed each other in the street, we should fail to recognise each other despite all our games and kisses in the past. To think that Loulou, who was the first to show me one of those aspects of that beauty which I was later to love above all others, is doubtless now an old woman with a marketing basket, like those one sees taking the air in the evening on benches in suburban boulevards. To think, too, that my mother whom I saw so young, so alive and so coquettish, is now, perhaps, as she lives in some small backwoods corner of the world, no more than a worn, slow-moving, serious-minded woman, so that I fear seeing her again ever. And, finally, to think that I was once that little boy, etc. . . . How many footsteps have effaced mine in those streets in which I walked, how many other children have played in those places I used to play! To think that it was all more than twenty years ago, more than twenty years since I lived there, breathed there, and that none of these things can be revived. Vanished beauty, eternal silence. And what impression will they make in another twenty years! But to hell with it, after all. When, having finished this book at last, I can recite verses again: '*De l'ancien Frascati vestale énamourée...*'; when I can go back to my friends ('Well, look who's here!') and be on the old terms with them again, in one place or another ('Stand me a drink, darling?') this melancholy will be soon forgotten and I shall start enjoying myself again with a vengeance. Besides, have I changed so much? My friends could bear witness to that: I do not walk easily; always a little tired, I should still like affectionate arms to carry me through life that I might avoid its shocks and its fatigues. I have kept the same character and almost the same tastes and, apart from two or three pleasures that are indispensable to me, such as literature—in which I do my best, though not caring over much—all else is more or less indifferent to me. I can still sit at home for hours on end without being bored, or among people without hearing them, concerned only with my own personality; and the Comédie-Française, too, where only the voice and beauty of Mlle Brandès stir me, remains the place where I sleep best. Yes, except physically—and what a difference there!—I am not far off being today just what that little boy was. He liked bright places, gay with popular tunes, where people walked to and fro, at once nonchalant and predatory, among scented women of easy virtue wearing rather loud dresses. When he was taken by chance to some Boule-Noire, some Elysée-Montmartre, or some Folies-Bergère, his happiness was such, though he could not express it, that he could almost have burst into tears. And now I, too, am happy only in those places full of light and music, hard, kaleidoscopic colours, and an acutely enervating atmosphere, through which drift the tendernesses, the sins, and the perfumes of a thousand brilliant, weary creatures, and I enjoy it all to the point of sadness. Get along with you, you old debauchee!

It sometimes seems to me that it would be a happiness to return to live in one of those streets in the Martyrs district where I once dreamed and idled away my days. When I think of the day I must go out of circulation, it is always in some wanton house of the Rue Saint-Georges, the Rue La Rochefoucauld or some similar street, that I see myself living, an old and not too worn beau, in company with a few women whose wantonness will adorn my old age. Oh, then I would resemble that little boy more than ever, ignorant once again, as he was ignorant, of the wretched follies that are called love. How sweet to end my life as I began it, and to close my eyes on the very landscape that filled the eyes of the child I was. And, on the morrow, I should make a last journey through the district, and on that day I would be carried; of that, I could be certain in advance. There is no doubt all this would be very splendid. And yet, who knows? Things may turn out quite differently. One day, I may be a famous writer, or an Academician. Life is so very odd! In the end, I may be taken with a dislike of dying and, in my search for the illusion of a more real life by continually changing my abode, may die elsewhere than in my own district. Even my tastes may change! But, in any case, I am quite certain that nothing will make me forget the little boy who was only happy with little girls or prostitutes, or by himself in his corner, and of whom I have said so little so as not to be a bore.

Chapter 4

Rue La Bruyère, quels caractères !
Quelles maximes, rue La Rochefoucauld !

GAVARNI

I am now going to write a little about some of my women
friends; the others will be for another day. The reader may,
to begin with, have been surprised at my feelings towards
them. To talk of one's mother and those sterile women in
the same breath! But that is why I wished to tell of some of
my childhood's memories. It was difficult to have a childhood like mine and not like these charming creatures later
on. There is nothing more formative than the society of
women; indeed, they frequently have a decisive influence on
one and something of it remains with one forever. I saw a
cartoon in an illustrated paper recently which showed a
little boy of six or seven and an elegant young woman; and
for caption: 'Tell me, Mama, are we going to the seaside
with the same Papa as last year?' I was brought up rather
like that. The sole difference was that it was a question of
mamas in my case. As you have seen, I had two already, the
real one and my old nurse, Marie, and I could have had
others, if I had paid attention to all the ladies who wanted
me to call them mama. 'Tell me, Papa, will the same Mama
as yesterday be here tomorrow?' I might have asked my
father, had my old nurse not warned me. There are many
memories of this kind behind the affection I have for my
women friends.

I shall therefore write a little about them. If it is not very good, at least it will not be very bad and, as far as they are concerned, it will give them pleasure. Then, I shall try to give a few details about our evenings together in one of those glittering places where they conduct themselves so harmoniously and carry on their profession in the most natural way in the world.

I shall start with Mlle Yvonne, a young person who has made much progress since the evening I first met her. It was in 1896, at the Nouvelle-Athènes. I was sitting in that café, having failed to find poor Perruche, of whom I will tell later, at the meeting-place we had arranged. Yvonne was sitting quite close to me, alone, her face that of a young girl, her manner somewhat artificial and her dress ugly. Not too ugly, however, with its rather English, half-proper, half-wanton look about it. In any case, she reminded me a little of that poem of Verlaine's: *Dansons la gigue!* I was so annoyed at having missed La Perruche, who was no doubt intimately engaged somewhere with one of her 'adored', and I was so bored moreover in that horrible café, that I signed to my neighbour to join me. In fact, had she not responded I would not have insisted. But, as if it were fated, she came over, and I then had to chat to her as one does chat on these occasions, saying nothing at all. How ingenuous she was and how clearly one saw from all the naïve, silly and right-thinking things she said that she was only a beginner! Really, when I come to think of it! Indeed, when I left her half an hour later, I regretted already having given her my address that she might come to see me the next day. The following day, it was even worse. As if I had invited her for the purpose, she got into bed as soon as she arrived, behaving exactly as if she were at home, too much as if she were at home. While I had dreamed of instructing her, of

52

having a young person to bring up in the way she should go! Nevertheless, I sat by the bed and tried, by giving her advice and endeavouring to educate her a little, to put her on the right path, etc. But it was a dead loss. With her legs in the air against the wall, Yvonne could talk only of her self-pity, of her desire to become an honest girl again, to return to her family and other such shocking things, while humming ridiculous songs out of tune. 'Doubtless,' I thought, 'to sing out of tune, is sometimes to sing correctly as Alexandre Dumas *fils* used to say.' Nevertheless, I had had enough of it and at about six o'clock in the evening, Yvonne having decided to get up, I let her go without even replying to her invitation to go to see her in some house or other in the Rue Lepic where she lived. A year went by, and I had almost forgotten her when, waiting one evening in front of the Olympia for yet another friend who was unpunctual, I saw this Yvonne out of the past coming towards me, looking so smart and assured that I scarcely recognised her. She gave me her hand, and as I complimented her on her transformation, she said: 'Oh, you were right, and you see how well I listened to you!' And she gave me her new address, expensive furnished lodgings in the Rue Fontaine. 'You'll be able to see how much I've changed,' she added, 'and, for you, you know. . . .' You can believe me or not as you like, but I have not yet made use of the invitation. Women are all very fine, indeed there is a song about it, but even in them stupidity is very difficult to forget. Yvonne may well have made the grade, wear extravagant hats, have her own furniture and plenty of trade, but she nevertheless remains for me the young idiot of the Nouvelle-Athènes. We are good friends, of course; we permit ourselves certain familiarities, but that is all, and she would find it very difficult to say what kind of a man I am. Does it annoy her? One might think so. Sometimes, as if by way of a joke, she renews her invitation to me to go and have a good time with her. 'You're making a mistake, you know!' she sometimes says, because of my reluctant air, allowing me to understand a whole lot of things with a few gestures. When we are alone, it does not matter, but there are often other people with us and I feel somewhat embarrassed. I then promise her to come on a certain day at a certain hour, without fail, and tell her she must have everything ready—and then I send a friend to whom I wish to do a good turn in my stead. I have such nice friends that Yvonne loses nothing by the substitution. At least, she has never complained. As for me, I am left in peace for a while and have friends who are always ready to do me a kindness.

Next, Mlle Marthe. She, indeed, knows all there is to know about her business. What delightful, well-regulated moments I owe her, and how warmly I should recommend her, if I were not afraid of appearing to have an interest in doing so! She has elegance, suppleness, firmness, all that seduces without leaving remorse behind, without counting that talent, which is rarer than you might believe, of knowing how to be silent at the right time. There are so many women who have a mania for talking at the critical moment! And with all this, she has preserved so beautiful a body, in spite of her thirty years past and all her love-life, that one might almost take her for a virgin, if a certain twist of the hips, all her own, did not prevent this mistake by revealing her knowledge after five minutes. All these are qualities which have gained for her the sympathy of a few rich old men who lavish every care on her and whom she still knows how to make use of, contrary to what Vauvenargues used to think. I do not wish to shock anyone, but I have often suspected Marthe of a certain lack of religion: at least she has the habit, as soon as she is in bed and before beginning to make love of exclaiming with a laugh: 'And now, down with the priests!' But perhaps she only says it for a joke? What is certain is that she never gets emotionally involved; the great emotions are not for her, and a man may as well be forewarned that, as far as she is concerned, he is never worth two. Intelligent and invariably composed, she has never loved nor desired to be loved. It is enough for her to give herself, to create happiness, to allow her beauty and her acts of beneficence to be enjoyed, to bring ever renewed care to pleasing and satisfying and, what is inestimable, her immodesty is scarcely obscene. She doesn't care a damn whether she is really appreciated or used merely for amusement. As she says so well herself, that is not the essential point. In a word, she is the perfect lover, who never makes a fuss, and to whom one returns when one has once known her.

I remember at this moment an evening with her when she had asked two friends and myself to dinner. I had brought with me a young man of about seventeen. I had met him in a library and dreamed of leading him astray. He was so sunk in his book, the young pedant, that I had promised myself to wake him up a bit. I had naturally not told him exactly where I was taking him. What an odd evening it was! Lennie was there, that poor Perruche and another woman whom I did not know. I had warned them, on arriving, of the character and youth of my guest, asking them to encourage him a little, without entirely over-stepping the bounds of propriety. I cannot assert that they preserved the proprieties altogether, but they were certainly as encouraging as it was possible to be. We had got barely half way through dinner when La Perruche, on the pretext of feeling hot, removed her corsage and continued dinner in her corsets, her arms bare, her breasts barely concealed by the lace of her chemise. You should have seen my young man's face. He was sitting next to La Perruche and dared not raise his eyes from his plate. Though he had talked a little at the beginning of dinner, he now fell silent, grossly insensible to all the attentions lavished on him. We were all even beginning to be a little embarrassed, and I don't know how things would have turned out, had the conversation not suddenly taken a serious turn due to an observation made by La Perruche, who said that my young friend no doubt lived at home.

'Oh, that's obvious,' cried Marthe, who was usually so reserved; 'I'm sure people have said hard things about us to Monsieur and told him not to frequent us. It's really so silly! As if we weren't as good as those married women, to whom these boys sooner or later all fall a prey. In the first place, though it's not for me to say so, we have a different sort of chic from them, and we don't make so much fuss. Besides, there's the fact that we're much less exhausting to men than those ladies with their vices. We know what love is, we do! You don't see us fluttering and gesticulating like a lot of geese in order to create an impression. We make only the necessary gestures . . . and when we do! We know how to lend ourselves to every whim, which you don't get with those ladies, I know, or at least it takes the hell of a time! And love with us is what it should be, a pleasure without weariness, the satisfaction of a need, the peace of the heart!'

After this sally, the conversation became frivolous again.

And now, Mlle Lennie who, to tell the truth, was never happy and was something of a Lesbian. I often think of the evening I first met her in the little restaurant in the Rue Pigalle where La Perruche, or Marcelle, had brought her. She was sitting a little apart when I arrived, like someone posing for a portrait, leaning back in her chair and smoking negligently. At first, I did not pay much attention to her; a woman more or less. . . . But, as I looked at her more closely, I was surprised at her resemblance to my mother, of whom I sometimes think when among these women. Yes, dark and pale-complexioned, her hair over her forehead down to the eyes, her nose a little arched, and her mouth a little thin, with very dark, rather troubled eyes, she was, without the frame, exactly like the picture I have at home of my mother at the age of about twenty-eight, her head leaning against the back of a sort of *chaise-longue*. It is a pity if you are interested in the emotion this resemblance aroused in me, for I shall have difficulty in explaining it. It was at once shyness, nostalgia and love. The little boy I had been was awakened in me and I would have liked at once to kiss this creature as he would have done and at the same time take her in my arms as a woman destined to give me more lively pleasures. I always took things slowly, as you have seen. Indeed, many evenings followed and Lennie and I knew each other already very well and yet I had not mentioned to her the family resemblance I saw in her. She was then living in the Rue Victor-Massé, a few yards away from that Passage Laferrière, where I had once visited my dear mama. Her friends had told her of my habits, and I sometimes went to see her at home, in the morning, about eleven o'clock, as if to help her get up. She smiled at me, as soon as I arrived, as if I were an idle friend who never

57

asked any sexual relations of her, though far from being conceited about it. I would sit down on her bed as she made room for me beside her and listen to her account of the evening before or other small-talk while caressing her breasts, one against the other, with my hand and such other parts of her as showed beneath the crumpled sheet. I was absorbed by the most wonderful of my memories, indeed so vividly that on several occasions I nearly became familiar. In my heart of hearts, I envied him, or her, who but an hour before had lain beside her and possessed her. Beauties surrendered to the first-comer, in which I imagined finding once more that charming body from which I was born! I wondered if that other had known how to love her as I would have loved her. To him she had been but the woman of a single night with whom he had amused himself as cheaply as possible. Perhaps what I was dreaming of was to have a friend. But, no matter. What would she say, if I told her, when I kissed her mouth, of the other face I was kissing in imagination at the same time as hers and, perhaps, with greater ardour? Perhaps she would throw me out and, for having wanted too much, I should have nothing at all. Good God! I would give her money if she asked for it! Yes, but after all would it be so great a pleasure? I know myself so well and how sometimes for months on end I enjoy the pleasures of being chaste. Just one more unpleasant nervous shock, as it is each time, and for so little sensual pleasure, while I invariably think of something else; without counting the inevitable remorse that follows immediately afterwards. Was it not perhaps the height of wisdom to be content with what I had? I thought about this for some time.

Then, one afternoon in the month of October 1897 or

1898, I was sitting with this enchanting strumpet on the terrace, almost deserted at that hour, of a wretched café in the Latin quarter. Due probably to a serious lack of money, Lennie's clothes, I now remember, were not very smart, and above all her hat, which was still a summer one, cried aloud to be changed. Having talked a little of this and that, we fell silent for a moment. Irresolute as was Titus concerning Bérénice, I gazed at this creature in whose company I spent so many hours that were at once filial and lover-like, since I desired her with ardour and yet avoided possessing her. No doubt, I was staring at her rather insistently, for she became aware of it. 'Oh,' she said, rather sadly, 'you've noticed that I haven't yet got a winter hat.' 'No,' I replied and, as if I were joking, I said: 'I'm merely thinking how very like my mother you look.' That was all, I had no idea how to go on. What I had said did not seem to affect Lennie very much and, no doubt, she was thinking much more about a new hat. I continued gazing at that face which brought alive for me so many dear and delicate features and I was filled with the memory of the day I had spent with my dear mama, who was so pretty and so elegant, and who had delighted me so much though I had not dared tell her so. Then, the moment came to go, and Lennie and I got to our feet. Generally, we parted casually, since we were nearly always due to meet that evening in some place or other. But how could I be calm after such a conversation? And when Lennie got into a cab, I said goodbye to her and left her, without even thinking of paying the cabby.

The next evening, when I met my women friends, I had a great success: 'Well, you have a fine time, don't you?' they said in chorus. But I could see from their manner that nothing was amiss between us. How different from my comrades earlier on, as indeed you can see! Of course, women are so intelligent! As for Lennie and I since that day. . . . But no, the proprieties must be preserved.

I have kept that delicious Perruche till the end, and it is certainly her turn, for she was so romantic and so wanton all her life. What's the use of telling how I met her? It was at once banal and charming. You meet a woman in the street, she pleases you, you talk to her, you don't displease her, she replies, you arrange a meeting, you go to bed together; sometimes it lasts a lifetime. Now that she is dead, there remain only the delicate lineaments that make up my memory of her to interest you. She had been around a good deal, mostly in places of ill-fame, such as the old Scarabée in the Faubourg Montmartre. Those were not rosy days, as she used to say; for indeed they were days when she was not always sure of her dinner, nor even of a bed. She had often waited for the coming of day in the Scarabée, in company with young habitués, who imagined, and they were not altogether wrong, that it was a question of financial rivalry. But all that was long ago, she had kept but a few lively expressions and a few obscene gestures, and yet she was a charming little girl. I had given her the nickname of Perruche, which in the end stuck to her, because of her passion for talking always about clothes. The fact is, she talked rarely of anything else. If one wanted to know what dresses would be worn this winter, or what hats would be fashionable next summer, or what the latest fashions were in trimmings on chemises, knickers or corsets, one could ask her. She knew as much about it as a shop assistant or a commercial traveller in fashions; and she would even go so far as to pose like a fashion-plate so as to demonstrate if you failed to understand. I have forgotten, too, her passion for

60

lace window-curtains, of which she also talked incessantly. Had I let her have her way, she would have put them up all over the place in my house. But these serious preoccupations had in no way diminished the grace of this pale child of the faubourgs, as they say in society. There was a constant smile on her fascinating mouth. You could surprise her any time, wake her suddenly in the middle of the night or in the morning, and she would give you that smile, always so ready, always the same. Oh, how she smiled! Some people thought she smiled even too much. Poor Perruche! With what compassion I fondle that slightly obscene picture of her now! How humble she was, in spite of all her chiffons, and what little importance she attached to giving herself! She was so unlike Marthe, whose sensible outlook I have recorded, for she could not live without loving and attaching herself to someone like a little dog. Even when she saw her companions of a night leaving in the morning, their senses satisfied, their eyes indifferent, she felt a certain emotion at the thought that, having enjoyed her, they would forget her nevertheless. But the worst times were when a friend of long-standing left her to get married or to change to someone else. Then, she became so tragically sentimental that she was inclined to talk of nothing less than drowning herself. It did not last long, of course, for, as she said: one lost, ten found; nevertheless, she suffered quite a lot. 'And to think I was counting on him to pay the rent!' she invariably said at these times; and she was quite despairing till she had really taken to somebody else. Then, she would bore you with her adored Georges, as she had bored you with her adored Edouard, and as she would bore you in the future with her adored somebody else. There were so many of these adored, of these 'chickabiddies', as she called them, that, in the end, one was inclined to confuse them and think they were all one and the same. Nevertheless, all these individual adorations never prevented her from treating anyone who came along with the utmost kindness. You did not have to insist much before she would show you that part of her body you wished to see. 'Do you want to see it?' she would simper. And before you could say knife you were seeing it, but she did it so naturally that there was never anything shocking about it. What more shall I say of her? She was not really beautiful nor, indeed, always very refined. Nor was she particularly intelligent. But you can't have everything. She had a certain grace, a certain aptitude; and she was easy to get on with. It was enough to make one love her, and one did love her. I remember one morning, having slept at her place, she brought me my coffee in bed, quite naked, one of her breasts hanging over the cup and the other over the sugar-basin, more or less. Later on, you will see how seriously infatuated she was with me and the excessively romantic way in which our love began. When her cheap strumpet's heart suffered a little or indeed much, and she felt that she was on the verge of being foolish, it was always to me she turned, so that I might console her, as an elder brother might a little sister without a lover. You may well wonder to what lengths these consolations were apt to lead us! The inconstant Perruche would emerge with her face drier, her hands less clenched, stretching herself like a young animal and declaring that, after all, 'it really didn't matter'.

'Not matter!' I replied sometimes, not knowing whether she was referring to her sorrows or the act in which we had been indulging. 'It's clear you have no literary ambitions such as mine.'

It would be an exaggeration, perhaps, to say that these creatures, both those I have written about and the others, are without faults. For instance, their statements are not always accurate, nor sometimes quite frank. They hide things from me, possess sums of money I do not suspect, ask my advice only to do precisely the opposite and then blame it on me if things go wrong. But their most annoying habit is quarrelling, sometimes like little girls, over nothing at all, merely to become the best of friends again five minutes later. The things I hear those evenings! Oh, loving women is not all roses, roses all the way! If only they would keep their quarrelling to themselves! But sometimes they attack me too, as if I had anything to do with their affairs; or, sometimes, because one of them has kicked up a row and I have tried to smooth things down. I am ashamed to say that at the start it rather annoyed me. 'If things are going to be like this. . . .' I thought; and it occurred to me, stupidly, that perhaps I could better use my evenings and my great impressionist talent elsewhere. Luckily, my friends knew how to bring me back to a more just appreciation of things. 'Haven't you finished showing off?' they would enquire delicately. 'Have you ever seen anything like it? . . . Now he's being a bore. . . . Really, it's too tiresome!' That was enough, and I calmed down. At bottom, I was too happy not to have to go back to my big books. What would I have done at home? Made literature? I was much happier with these women, thinking of the charming memories of long ago. These creatures, due to so many recollections, were so close to my heart, and essentially I was so like them! Were they not already weary before setting to work, did they not cultivate desire without much feeling it themselves, and make only the

63

gestures of love, as I, more often than not, make in literature but the mental cerebration? Oh, to know how not to get too involved in order not to use oneself up too quickly, to know how to say things to all comers without revealing one's secret, as these women so unconcernedly give pleasure, merely laughing afterwards at the grimaces they have witnessed. It serves so little purpose to be generous, good, devoted, grateful and loyal—those are weaknesses, at most!—and apart from a few sensitive and intelligent people on whom one chances occasionally, life is so full of the cads, the vulgar and the stupid. My friends moulded me without realising it, or rather they taught me to make of myself what I wished. And now, when they quarrel, I give no sign. They can shout, insult me, tell me to get out and so on, but as far as I'm concerned it's like water off a duck's back. To see me, you would swear that I do not even know them, so great is my serenity. You may say all this is not very pretty. Oh, but it's because you do not know what it is to love!

In the early days, I frequently resembled people whom they had known and who had since died or married or gone away, or they didn't know what had become of them. It is such a good way of starting a conversation for them, this pretending to take you for someone else, and telling you what an extraordinary likeness you bear to someone they have loved in the past! We sometimes talked of these gentlemen friends, when something or other reminded them of them, illness or financial embarrassment. Some of them had achieved good positions in life, and this flattered them even though they no longer saw them. When talking to me, they adopted an intimate air, mentioned their family, what they might have been, had they so wished, and had

64

fe not been so damnable. It was always the same old story:
I was the daughter of a senior officer. . . .' (As if that was
nything to boast about!) 'My mother was a very good
voman. . . .' But they no longer talk such nonsense to
1e now.

I remember the minor sentimental miseries I carried
bout with me at that time: the coquetry, in the past, of my
ttle childhood friends, the recent defection of a charming
nistress, and the still more recent fatuity of having lacked
he courage to embrace certain young persons with
omplexions of peaches and roses. It was not love I sought
rom these women. My literary projects fatigued me
quite enough. It was grace and charm, something to relieve
he dreariness of my days spent working among people
acking in tenderness. I was treated as you may imagine.
They talked their nonsense and I told them of my
mpotence. 'Do you think it's fun always sleeping with
•eople you don't know?' they would say. 'It's the same
vith me,' I would reply; 'at a distance, I want it and get
excited, I think how splendid it will be. But when I come to
t, nothing happens!' Pleasure without pleasure, both for
hem and me, I would add to myself. How close to them I
elt at these times, I whose pleasures are but of five minutes
duration! Sometimes, too, they would make themselves
comfortable, and one of them would expose a pale, pure
breast, arousing my tenderness. Unable to control myself,
I would get to my feet and kiss its enchanting pallor. 'Oh,
ow like you!' they would say, immediately unbuttoning
hemselves still further. 'You simply can't see a breast
vithout at once. . . .' 'What do you expect?' I would reply
by way of excuse. 'We are all devout in our own way.'

These things were really all pleasures, but I had sorrows

too. I shall not recount them, it would take too long, and I have already revealed the old Adam enough. Nevertheless so that you may judge. . . .

As I have said, an extremely agreeable mistress had left me a little while before, seduced by the spiritual appearance of a singer in musical-comedy, who was fairly well-known and whom she afterwards married. I languished absurdly, thinking that no other woman could replace her, that my sorrow would last for the rest of my life, in brief, all the usual absurdities. I took it all so seriously that I had written a number of poems about it that were neither good nor bad; they were just the sort of things you might expect; they made no mark, and the people who read them cannot have been much impressed. It appeared, however, that a lady to whom my father was giving lessons in acting, that she might show off on the stage by declaiming pompous and boring things, thought they were rather good. Had I known in time, I would have given her the little notebook in which I had collected them under the title of *Le Petit livre ridicule*, and which I had destroyed. But my masterpiece was a little prose work somewhat after the style of the *Rêverie de Léolin*, in the *Eau de Jouvence*. It had not cost me a great deal of trouble for at that time I wrote with great facility, but it had the advantage over my verses of giving me something to think about when with my friends, particularly on the days when laziness had prevented their going out and they began playing cards towards the end of the evening. It began to be late. 'The street was deserted and gave on to the Trinity.' Being unable to play, I found myself rather isolated, in spite of the slate and pencil they gave me to keep the score. The cards fell in lively fashion, amid laughter, exclamations and even a little abuse. My friends were enjoying themselves! Therefore, to occupy myself a little, I let my poetic frenzy carry me away.

'Oh, those evenings in spring-time, and in winter too, high up in the Faubourg Saint-Jacques, where we fell asleep together, my boyish face resting between your breasts. There was a little mole on one of them, the right, I think. And nearly every night, after other things, I would kiss this tiny blemish.

'How many men have possessed you, since you left me? What do you think of that married life, in which you are now at rest from so many changes, so many meetings, those at the tram stop in the Place du Châtelet, for instance, when you were waiting for your singer? And how is that little girl, of whom perhaps I am the father? Do you sometimes think of our pleasures in that narrow little room in the half-empty house, or have you forgotten it all? Is it true that women never forget their first lover? Are you still capable of loving?

'The power of the literary imagination! I can see her now as she was in the past. Yes, if I so wish it, you, who were the first, are present to me. Your face is smiling as it used to do, your eyes are still the eyes I loved, and there are no lines on your brow beneath that mass of auburn hair so shot with gold. Do you remember how you used to change the doormats from storey to storey in the houses to which we went? However much I scolded you each time, you always did it again. And when we began again, on the 14th July 1895, after more than two years of separation? You were not yet married. Your singer was on tour. For several weeks I had been courting you, as in the early days, when I was eighteen and you were twenty-three. I used to take you home at night to the Rue Bailiff. We used to go down the old Rue Saint-Jacques and stop for a moment in the little dark alley which runs behind the Collège de France; there we would embrace and then set off again, as far as your front door. At last, on that 14th July, you surrendered to me utterly. Do you remember our making love on the floor of my hotel room in the Rue de Savoie? It lasted two or three months before he came back, and then it was good-bye! Oh, pale, dancer's body, how I loved you! Oh, don't make a fuss, I may at least embrace you! After so long, it cannot affect you much! And stay a little, so that we can talk. What changes have taken place in me since our love, what other loves of a month, a week, a night, and now but a long chastity! And yet, if you so wished, my fondest caresses would still be yours. You don't believe me, you shake your head like someone who has already been deceived. These women about me surprise you? At first, you did not see them, and now that you have you don't know what to think and you're embarrassed. There is really no reason for it. If you only knew. . . . These women resemble you. Each one of them has some quality of yours, one your coquetry, another your sensuality, that one your folly, and all a shapeliness of the hips worth yours. Come nearer, sit down beside them. They are your sisters, they are what you once were for a little time, what you would have done much better to remain, instead of getting married: sweet vessels of pleasure and melancholy. It was they who consoled me, when I was grieving for you with phrases from novels and verses from our best poets, and in their arms, those first times, it was still a little to you that I was making love. It even sometimes happened that, in sensual moments, I would call them by your name. . . . Oh, stay a little longer! We shall be going soon. We'll take a cab. You can tell your husband that you stayed at your mother's, or you can simply go home a few hours later. You won't make me believe that you have never deceived him. Besides, with me, it's not the same thing. Please, let me love you again a little, as in the old days. You will, won't you? You'll come? . . .

'What are you saying? That you're married, that you've got children, that you love your husband, that your mother is a respectable woman, and that you simply must go home? . . . Oh, really, you're still the same, you haven't changed at all!'

How romantic I was! I should find it very difficult to write in that tone today. It is true that the girl I was celebrating so sentimentally has changed much. In the first place, she is no longer young. And, already inclined to stoutness then, she has now become quite the married woman. When I go down the Rue Notre-Dame-de-Lorette, I see her sometimes on her balcony on the fifth floor of a house full of midwives. 'To think I was once mad about her!' I say to myself as I look at her, and I feel rather sad at the size she has become. Recently, I chanced to walk behind her down the Rue Saint-Lazare, the Rue de la Chaussée-d'Antin and the Rue Lafayette for over half an hour. Did she recognise me? . . . When I had passed her, I stopped at a shop to wait for her; she came and stopped there too. I crossed the street, she crossed it. We went on like this as far as the corner of the Rue de Châteaudun and the Rue Le Peletier. Perhaps I should have spoken to her, suggested a ride in a cab. Who knows, it might have given her pleasure? Besides, her little girl, who is a little mine

69

too, must be beginning to be charming! However, I said nothing, and when we arrived at the Faubourg Montmartre, as I was not going her way, I left her. It was better so. I should find it difficult to become enthusiastic about her all over again; it is bad enough to have done so once more. Perhaps, indeed, I should have done better not to mention her here, so as not to excite my friends, and to have written instead that *Essay on Onanism*, which I have so long promised them for their amusement. But there it is! By finding that manuscript with its piece of prose, I have had two whole pages ready written. Whereas I should have had to write the whole *Essay*. For once, I did not hesitate.

Chapter 5

*The most wasted of days is that on which
one has not laughed.*

CHAMFORT

As I start writing about them, I pause for a moment
to look back on the lights, the floor-shows, the women,
the habitués, all the brightly coloured movement of those
places of pleasure, where I sometimes spent the evening
with my women friends. The Folies-Bergère, the Palais de
Glace, the Casino de Paris, the Olympia, the Jardin de
Paris, the Marigny, and how many more; and I can see
them in my mind's eye as if I were there in reality. The
clear, coruscating beauty of those places was like brilliantly
illuminated looking-glasses. Formerly, they were the
Elysée-Montmartre, the Ambassadeur, the Tivoli Vauxhall,
the Skating, the Boule-Noire; and, before that, the Mabille,
the Casino, the Courtille, the Closerie, the Reine Blanche;
and, before that again, the Frascati, the Valentino, the
Prado; and, even earlier still, the Idalie, the Tivoli,
the Folies, the Paphos. All these names, evoking, pro-
claiming indeed, a life of rhythm and movement, of jewels,
music, dancing, libertinage, frivolity, idleness, warmth and
perfume, are redolent of a charm and even charged with
an emotion that, as far as I am concerned, have no rivals.

I cannot help it if people are astonished or if others
think I shall tire of them in the end. Have they never felt
the excitement of those shimmering scenes? Perhaps they
know only evenings of books and study in their closed

rooms. I wish them joy of them. As for me, I have done
with them, having found no pleasure in them, the kind of
pleasure I sought. How bored I was for nearly ten years
as I read the masterpieces and pretended to enjoy them
while seeking joy in vain. You won't catch me at it again.
Besides, I derived no benefit from it nor even ideas. At most
merely the pleasure of getting into the skin of such and such
a writer and playing, for a moment, the celebrated game
his way. These books revealed to me their authors' unin-
spired labours and their puerile desire to astonish, but
nothing to touch the heart. Whereas those places I have
described, as soon as I had determined to get to know them,
filled me at once with an emotion particular to me, that is
to say, one that had nothing whatever to do with a desire
for admiration or imitation. There, at least, I found and
recognised myself, certain, this time, of having made no
mistake, so much did I resemble the little boy I had been,
but with his tastes a little broadened, his tenderness more
emotional, his timidity more sensitive, and even his shyness
exorcised by these bright scenes. It was all familiar to me,
easy, like some well-known landscape to which I was
returning. And what intellectual pleasures I found there
too, though I prefer to keep them to myself, in order not to
be accused of affectation. Certainly, at my death, I want the
dancers from one of these places at my funeral.

I often tell myself that the *Valse bleue* marks a date in
my life; and this is intended more seriously than you
might think. How La Perruche enchanted me with
that tune! . . . No sooner had she got up than she began
". . . *Pourquoi ne plus m'aimer, tu sais bien que je t'aime* . . .'
To tell the truth, I found it rather difficult to get accustomed
to these tunes at first. I was so full of my big books, so

preoccupied with such high matters! But the day soon came when I felt the charm of these unimportant tunes; you get them on the brain without realising it, and hum them unconsciously, while thinking of something else. After all, I thought, they have their own peculiar character. They are also part of life, this fine life we all waste more or less, as if it were to last for ever. For life does not consist only of great art, duty and one's family, but also of fantasy, pleasure and young persons who are yielding without being clinging. Besides, everyone to his own life. For some, important works of great scope worthy of their distinguished format; for others, everyday life with its brief pleasures. The important thing is to tread one's own path. It all comes to the same in the end. . . . '*Pourquoi ne plus m'aimer*. . . .'" Alas, poor Perruche!

What tunes there were besides, even better than these: *Valse des Roses, Beau Danube Bleu, Amant d'Amanda, Tzarine, Marche Lorraine, España, Marche des Petits Pierrots, Polka des Anglais, Valse bleue, Froufrou, Marjolaine, Franchesa, Sourire d'avril, L'Amour boiteux, Tiger Lily,* and so many, many others, which gave those places, décors and habitués the rhythm that suited them. How they matched the spirit and sensibility (and they are one) you brought to these places, the frivolity, raillery, nonchalance, the gestures of invitation, the drinks solicited—'Are you standing me a drink, Monsieur ? . . .'—sometimes accorded, sometimes refused, proposals exchanged, prices argued, addresses asked for and given, colloquies in which only certain gestures were lacking to make them in themselves an act of love, lounging, idleness. . . .

The Folies-Bergère above all. I, who am so difficult to see during the day because of my many occupations—

family, correspondence, business—and my numerous preoccupations—fame, decorations, the Academy—am often to be found there at about ten o'clock at night, sometimes alone, sometimes with two or three women friends. According to the time of year, I go sometimes to the Palais de Glace, to the Casino de Paris, to the Marigny or elsewhere. But, more often than not, it is in the Folies-Bergère I spend my nights whenever I can. And what nights! The only thing that is rather a bore about it is the distance I have to go home, when none of my friends takes me back with her. Luckily, this is a very rare occurrence, and I nearly always go to sleep in the district of my childhood with one of them. Yes, what nights, I repeat! I sit or wander to and fro not far from my women friends, without seeming to. They themselves either sit or walk up and down, making eyes to right and left and smiling more or less at everyone. I follow their subtle game from afar, watch them pose their glances like great flowers, and assume a variety of attitudes according to whether they have to do with an habitué or a stranger, a difficult old man or an unfledged boy, a foreigner or a Parisian. From time to time I pass one of them, or two, or three. If they are free, we exchange news and criticise the appearance of the people who pass by; if they are not, we smile as we pass each other, make a little sign, our heads turned, and move on. My literary appearance prevents this behaviour having an equivocal air in the eyes of fools. Indeed, I have become so clever at it that I look like some idiot who won't go along.

Sometimes again, I isolate myself, leaving my friends to do the best they can, and then I think only of myself. I abandon myself to my own pleasure, to my memories of childhood, to my delight in the scene, enjoying the reflec-

ions in the mirrors, the combinations of colours, the
ndlessly varied movement of the crowd, and the
tmosphere of mingled langour and activity. Oh, how I
njoy the reflection of my pale face under the brilliant
lectric lights on these nights! Standing motionless in that
place I have mentioned on the promenade of the big hall,
I think more than ever of the child I was and of his pretty
mama, allowing myself to be jostled by the idlers and seeing
nothing of what is happening on the stage but a vague
luminous movement. What a delight it is and one not within
everyone's reach! And what a pity that she should be
married somewhere, instead of being still here with me, my
darling mama! She would be one friend the more and
perhaps the best.

Or again, I choose a comfortable arm-chair on the promenade of the hall, placed so as to lose nothing of the
thousand-fold play of lights, colours and groups of people.
The orchestra diffuses its light music, pianissimo during
the floor-show, and loud, vibrant, almost hysterically
exciting during the interval. More in love with myself than
ever, I enjoy all this effortlessly through my cigarette
smoke. I care nothing for the masterpieces of French
literature at these moments. I am a prey to reveries in which
beauty and money worries, thoughts of glory and modesty,
flashes of talent and phrases of others, tenderness and
casualness, scepticism and emotion are all mingled. Am I
amused? Am I bored? I should find it hard to say. But that
I am perfectly happy is almost a dogma. Women pass and
pass again, never the same, so flexible are they, casting their
grace and their bright colours among my reveries, and time
goes by so quickly, alas, and yet so sweetly! But it begins
to grow late, sober people are going home, the music

becomes veiled, and the lights also. Now, there are but a few groups gradually breaking up, a few women glancing round the clear, gleaming space, and then, sometimes, a sort of madness seizes me, a sort of haze, something similar to Phèdre's disquiet: '*Que ces vains ornements, que ces voiles me pèsent!*' Memories, so distant yet so present, lapsed affections which have left their mark on me, faces loved and lost but never forgotten, the buried dead who emphasise the fact that one is growing older, books dreamed of so much that one will never write them, these scenes full of light, mirrors, scents and rhythms, these women, all a little damaged somewhere or other, and the little boy from the past, shy and sensitive, and the little girls who were so coquettish with him, and his mother too, so unforgettably dear, and how much more; they all dance wildly through my head, a vivid and melancholy ballet, and I think of the death of all this wealth of pleasure and sorrow that is beauty itself, I am sure of it, I feel it, so live and affecting a beauty, that it stirs me to the very verge of weeping; but, alas, no tears flow! At these moments, I have never enough paper on me to make notes. Moreover, as the place is about to close, I am nearly always disturbed by one of my friends who has done nothing and thinks of me. 'Really, darling,' she interrupts me, 'aren't you coming?' So I get up and follow her. 'How can I be expected to work?' I think, as I go off. 'I'm always being interrupted!'

The Jardin de Paris is also dear to me, and you will soon see why. How many lyrics I have heard there in which *true* rhymed with *you*, *love* with *above*, *eyes* with *skies*, *spring* with *ring*, and *etc.* with *etc!* . . . Anyway, one has to spend one's nights somehow. It's not everyone who can go to the Universités Populaires and *teach* beauty. How often I have amused myself by sliding into the basement down that well-known slide! I have sometimes spent whole evenings doing nothing else: slide, run to the stairs, climb them, slide down again. . . . I know very well on these occasions that my heart disease is growing worse, and even, sometimes, after eight or ten turns, that it is becoming very bad indeed. But, to hell with it! What does life matter? And isn't what I'm doing living after all! It gives my friends so much pleasure to give me a hard push and see me slide down in the twinkling of an eye, sometimes on my stomach, sometimes on my back, my legs hanging or spread wide, my arms in the air or crossed on my chest. One, two, three . . . and off you go! Oh, those delicious evenings! What laughter, shouts and indecent gestures! What fun it is! The people watching us with idiotic expressions on their faces can't get over it.

And when the concert is over and three or four women begin dancing the *chahut* on the floor round the orchestra! What very special moments I have spent there, without seeming to, my elbows on the balustrade and my chin in my hands, watching the wanton grace of these women, with their quick, harmonious movements, their art as precise as a drawing. In the end, we got to know each other and said good evening as friends. What makes these dances stir up so many emotions in me, affecting me, transporting me like a poem or a fine symphony? I have often wondered as I stood at the balustrade or in other places when I have watched other women dancing the *chahut*. On these occasions, my feet itch, I feel the devil seize on my body and my body respond to the rhythm, my mind capers and dances, and the impulse is so strong, that I have to restrain myself with my whole will from springing straight on to

77

the narrow dance-floor and waving my arms and doing the splits among the kicking legs and cunningly raised skirts of these creatures to whom I feel so close in a thousand indefinable ways, at once in tastes, memories and desires. Oh, and when they have finished and go to have a drink and try, in their turn, to turn their romantic hearts to account, it seems to me sometimes that I am more exhausted than they are!

It was at the Jardin de Paris one night that I had a lot of trouble with La Perruche. She, Lennie, Marthe and I were there. It was towards the end of the summer of 1899. I had been spending a few days in my family's village—one hundred and twenty-one inhabitants—and, rather bored, I had written to my friends to meet me at the Jardin de Paris where I would go and relax a little when I came off the train. Yvonne and Suzanne were very busy and could not come. It was about half past ten, when I arrived. The first part of the concert was just over. Everyone was in the garden. I can still remember the tune the orchestra was playing when I arrived that night, a mediocre but catchy tune, and I can still see my friends coming towards me, walking a little in time to it.

Before going further, I must explain that at that time I enjoyed a certain prestige among my friends, a literary prestige, be it understood, for I shall never enjoy prestige of any other kind. Jean de Tinan, so charming and so dear to me, had been dead for about a year. His last unfinished novel, *Aimienne ou le détournement de Mineure*, had just been published posthumously and, on the basis of this book, which is a great deal better than it seems at first sight, I had written a few hurried pages on my dead friend which had appeared in the August *Mercure*. I had read these to my women friends and, whether it was from astonishment that I had done some work or pleasure at the few words I had said about them in passing, they had since shown me a certain consideration. La Perruche, in particular, never stopped talking about the book, assuming more than ever the postures of fashion-plates, and predicting a great future for me, if I would only work! 'You know, it's not really as deep as all that,' she said when she really got going. 'You know, I simply don't believe you can't do as well as that, you know the fellow I mean, the one who wrote that book about people making love in front of pictures, intellectual soul-mates and all that. Really, if he thinks what he's written's funny! Of course, if it amuses Versailles, well! And the fellow who wrote that book, you know, the book etc., etc.' This is what happens when you lend books by people you know: one hears things said of them which one thinks in one's own innermost thoughts. Indeed, La Perruche encouraged me a lot. And, in order to shut her up, I had even made her a present of a copy of Tinan's novel, in a fine binding, with the five or six pages I had written bound in at the end. But even this had not sufficed and, in order to get a little peace, I had had to summon up all my talent to write her a long dedication, which she made me begin over again three times, since she never thought it seemly enough. Could I but find them, I would quote the lines I wrote specially for that charming girl here.

I can say, therefore, that since I had written that article, my women friends handled me with their gloves on. At difficult moments, they weren't quite so quick to pick on me. To say that I congratulated myself on this progress, however, would be an exaggeration. I never had so many letters to write for them as during the five or six months following on the article's publication. 'That fellow's really such a bore! Write him a letter telling him I won't have anything more to do with him. You can sign my name.' Besides, they never ceased from saying: 'Well, aren't you going to write something else?' Naturally, I didn't answer or scarcely, contenting myself with whistling and telling them to leave me alone. 'Of course, I do see it's difficult for you,' they would then say amiably. Oh, how right it is to say that fame has its tiresome aspects! Only La Perruche did not reproach me. It was as if she understood what literature is, and that one usually feels inclined to work only when away from one's desk. 'He's like me,' she must have thought to herself. 'When I'm alone, I want someone to love me and as soon as I have a man in my arms I wish it were another.' How often I talked of this to her, when her friends had reproached me more than usual! 'At least, my dear Perruche, you understand,' I would say to her. 'You understand, don't you? I'm no more than an essayist. Besides, I rarely carry anything through to the end in any field.'

So, there we were that night, Lennie, Marthe, La Perruche and I sitting in the Jardin de Paris. Since it was two or three weeks since I had seen them, it was a real pleasure to be with them and back amid those scenes that are so dear to me. We must all have been thinking of matters of high moment, for we barely spoke at all. For my part, sitting in an arm-chair with my legs propped on another, I was thinking of the profound boredom aroused by the works of M. Anatole France. From where she was sitting, Lennie was making eyes at a handsome, elderly gentleman a few seats away. Marthe was sitting opposite me, her head bent a little forward, her hands covered with rings and holding her umbrella. Her face was beginning to show those slight discolorations about the nostrils and eyes, near the ears and at the corners of the mouth, which announce the end of beauty. They lent her features a more delicate and, indeed, a more moving quality, a sort of serenity, a resigned regret, a poignant sweetness. How moved I was to see her so tired and worn! 'Fading beauty is more beautiful and more disturbing than the beauty of youth!' I thought as I looked at her. 'There's another in whom I could have rejoiced and who will soon have to retire now. None of it makes us any younger!' I should no doubt have pursued these reflections had Marthe not got up to take a turn with Lennie, in order to try to persuade the handsome old gentleman who seemed unwilling to go along. I stayed alone with La Perruche, who was sitting close to me. The orchestra was playing that catchy tune from *Franchesa*: 'Ah! ah! ah! ah! ah! ah! ah! ah!' etc. Whenever I think of that evening, I find myself humming that popular tune. Had anyone told me the conversation I began with La Perruche about a bolero she wanted to buy was to end as it did, I wouldn't have believed them! Of course, I was very fond of La Perruche and I knew, too, that she was not indifferent towards me. But an emotional scene merely on the strength of that! When I think of it now, all sorts of things come back to me. La Perruche must have been seeking the opportunity for a long time. In any case, I was not expecting this sentimental conversation into which she put all her charm.

'I like you, you know,' she said suddenly, after talking of quite different matters. 'If you wanted, we could make love.'

'Oh, good Lord,' I said. 'If you want to. . . .'

'Will you come and see me properly one afternoon?'

'Yes, if you like, but when?'

'I'll tell you the story of my life.'

'That'll be gay!'

'You can give me advice.'

'What will you pay for that? . . .'

'And then, when I've got no one else with me, you'll be able to come.'

'All the same, I wouldn't want. . . .'

'We can go out together.'

'Where? . . .'

'I'm a good girl, you know. At bottom, I've got a heart. I could even fall in love, once and for all. Perhaps one day you'll love me too. Can one ever tell?'

'That's certainly true! Can one ever tell?'

'Will you, then? . . .'

But these passionate moments are more finally over than you might suppose. La Perruche had been ill for some time already, and she would have done better to rest, rather than give herself to all comers and gad about all over the place at night. Everyone told her so, her doctor, her friends and I. But no! It was too natural to her to give pleasure, her need to love and be loved was too strong, and she was too much the rage to be able to moderate her life. 'I hardly have a moment to myself,' she wrote to me at this time to cancel an appointment: 'as soon as one's gone, another arrives. I should have to cut myself in a dozen pieces to satisfy all the boys.' And, on another occasion (I leave out the more intimate passages): 'What I feared has happened. That big Georges of mine has just said he wants to come to see me tomorrow, and as I've no cash and he'll probably bring some, I can't tell him to go to hell. You see, woman proposes but man disposes. I'm so sorry because, the day after tomorrow, I shall no doubt be indisposed,' etc., etc.

Then there happened what was bound to happen: all this complaisance did La Perruche a bad turn. On Sunday, 29th October, we had gone to the Comédie-Française together. That night they were playing a piece by Hugo or Dumas *fils*, I really can't remember which. I had told La Perruche that it was terribly boring and she wanted to see if I was right. During the interval, at about eleven o'clock, she was seized with violent pains in the stomach and with a fairly serious haemorrhage. As this happened two days after her period was over, it was disquieting enough. Without waiting for the end of the play—that, at least, was something gained—we went back to her flat, in the Place Vintimille, where she had been living for only a fortnight, in a house where it was forbidden to use too much water. She went to bed at once, and the night went by, she suffering like a wounded animal, and I walking up and down the room, not knowing what to do and rather worried about her pain which I could do nothing to relieve. The next morning the doctor came and examined her; it was metritis, and serious; curetting would be necessary. In the meantime, he gave her a prescription, but nothing could relieve La Perruche's pain. I sent for another doctor, then a third. But throughout, La Perruche continued suffering just as much, and I continued nursing her, giving news to people who came to enquire and doing the house-keeping. Lord, the injections I gave her, the poultices I made, the suppositories I administered, the medicines I made her drink! I can still see myself in my white apron, with my syringe, pills and phials. The only thing that relieved her a little I discovered for myself: towels soaked in boiling water and applied to her stomach for as long as she could bear them. Oh, I know all about nursing women now, I can promise you that! At last, as she got no better, I had to follow the doctor's advice and take La Perruche to the hospital, where she would be better off for the operation that might make her well. It was the 4th November. The kind creature had been in bed for six days, and I was beginning to get accustomed to seeing her suffer. The night before, sitting by her bed, I wrote on the bedside table, between two injections, the short article that appeared in the *Mercure* the following month, on a book by M. Pierre Quillard. But now it was over. I had to leave it all. I should no longer be looked at with interest in the house as a good young man who was exhausting himself nursing his mistress. I should no longer amuse myself each morning by going to buy biscuits and wine, or by gazing at the two little wax faces, so alive, their hair so beautifully dressed, in the hairdresser's on the ground floor of No. 51, Rue de Douai. And, as I smoked cigarettes by the window, I should no longer see Berlioz, standing in the square with that bored expression he has worn so long, and surrounded at midday by cabs for hire. Poor little bedroom! It was so gay and elegant, and La Perruche and I had arranged it together! It had hardly been worth quarrelling all the time about where each object should be placed! Who knew whether she would ever return there now? I need hardly say, it was a bad moment to live through.

After luncheon, about one o'clock, I sent for a cab. Helped by the cabby, I got poor Perruche out of bed and we took her down the five storeys as gently as we could. Half way down, she suddenly fainted on the stairs, and a woman, who lived in the house and knew her to be ill, came out on to the landing with smelling salts. What a journey it was from the Place Vintimille to Lariboisière! La Perruche lay back in the cab, covered with blankets, and I held her clenched and feverish hands in mine. Pale, yellow even, her features drawn, her fine eyes still full of sweetness, she gazed at me speechlessly, shaken with sobs and stifled moans. How far away were all our frivolity, our raillery, our wantonness and how distant, too, were the pleasures on which we had but scarcely embarked. 'Well, old lady,' I said, trying to amuse her, 'it's not so funny, eh?' And I stared out at the streets as they jerked past the window, the Rue de Douai, the Rue Victor-Massé, the Rue Condorcet, the Rue de Maubeuge and so on. At last, we arrived. After the usual formalities, which merely took a couple of hours, while we waited in an icy hall, they appointed a ward and a bed, the Bernutz ward, bed No. 11 and La Perruche was taken upstairs and put to bed. When it was done, I went in, kissed her and said: 'See you tomorrow.' Then I left. That popular song, the *Valse bleue*, was running through my head in spite of myself as I went back to the Rue Bonaparte, where I was then living.

I went to see La Perruche every day. She was getting no better; on the contrary, there were complications, peritonitis, and I don't know what else; anyway, what's the point of going into all the details. In a bed not far from hers, on the other side of the ward, was a dirty and fantastically wrinkled old woman, suffering from syphilis who never ceased moaning. I saw her die there without being really much aware of it. She had been groaning—*ah! ah!*—all day since morning, rolling her head continuously from side to side in a sort of jerky, rhythmic movement. It entertained the patients a little. There are so few pleasures in a hospital ward! I have often thought since of the way that old woman went *ah! ah!* as she lay dying. It was not so tuneful or so full of wonder as the *ah! ah!*'s my old nurse used to sing to make me go to sleep. Nor so tender and loving as the *ah! ah!*'s of La Perruche in her amorous moments, when she called you 'darling' over and over again. Nor so lively, bright and catchy as the *ah! ah!*'s of music-hall tunes. Nevertheless, they were not so remote from these. For something both maddening and tragic, too, related these *ah! ah!*'s to each other in my mind. Happy, indeed, are they who can die uttering rhythmic, if unconscious, *ah! ah!*'s. With a faint sound of music not too far away, or even without music, they become almost a tune, a tune to send you to sleep. What a perfect Sunday's rest after all the happy weeks of life! And what a splendid precedent into the bargain! Like everyone else, you have made a fool of yourself, uttered innumerable words, worked and made love, laughed, wept, done the best you could, then, swish, down comes the curtain, carry out the body, the play's over. Nothing has mattered overmuch and you're the first to think of it no more.

It was rather like this La Perruche died one day, the 26th November, at about eleven o'clock in the morning, just in time for me still to be able to go out to luncheon. I had been warned at home that she was very ill and, as soon as I arrived, the sister told me it was the end. I went to her bedside. She seemed hardly to be suffering so very ill was she, and in her charming eyes, from which so many scenes were to fade, there appeared nothing now but a gentle lassitude. The sister was standing opposite me, on the further side of the bed, her complexion bright, obviously in splendid health. 'How wholesome!' I thought, looking at her buxom curves that might have had their value for

86

someone other than myself. You should have seen her knowledgeable air, how she noted the progress of the illness, how she winked. 'You're much better,' she said, used as she was to trying to deceive the patients, 'much better! By tomorrow, she'll be completely cured.' 'I believe you,' I thought, 'she'll be cured by tomorrow all right. Indeed, she'll be cured much sooner than that.' Then someone suggested summoning the priest to give La Perruche the last sacraments. I was dismayed at the idea of seeing the representative of every lie and superstition beside La Perruche, who had never been other than spontaneous and frivolous. Did she require these cere-monies, this creature who had never stood on ceremony in her life? Could she not be allowed to slip away in peace, merely sighing a little as if still making love? Fortunately, La Perruche had heard and would have nothing to do with it. 'I have never done anyone any harm,' she whispered. 'I require nothing, I'm ready to go.' Done any harm! She? Poor Perruche! Indeed, she might have said that she had done nothing but good, and to so many people, and not always for very much money! For it was there that all her merit lay, in doing good, and she was paying dearly for having had a few bright feathers, by dying thus in a hospital bed, spoiled and emaciated, with only me at her bedside and, at the bed's foot, the sister with her robust, ebullient health.

Thus she died, and a kindly patient two or three beds away said that, after all, it was no great loss. She was buried next day, as casually as if one were going for a walk, and no one thought any more about it. It is true, indeed, that great sorrows are dumb! Poor Perruche! She sleeps now in that frightful cemetery outside Paris, beyond the Barrière de Saint-Ouen, where I have always thought my old nurse Marie must have been buried. There were not many people there, I must say. There were no more than a dozen of us behind the hearse; not one of her more serious clients: only a few women friends, her concierge and myself. And she who thought only of sparkling, pleasing and being loved has a poor and narrow grave on which the flowers are but seldom renewed. Besides, it's so far away and quite a business to get there. Nevertheless, I sometimes go either alone or with a friend, when I feel in melancholy mood. I buy little cakes to eat on the way, and a bunch of flowers for a few pennies to decorate the grave. Standing there motionless and smiling, appearing rather silly to the people round about, the memory of La Perruche revives in me in all its detail. I remember those breasts I knew so well and caressed and kissed so ardently, those charming arms, that clever mouth, those legs that were so popular, all that compliant rather urchin body. Her easy beauty, which excited so many people, her gracious gestures, her perpetual smile, her far from displeasing obscenities, how far away they all are! To think that we rejoiced in each other, that I held her in my arms, even though it sometimes prevented my going to sleep, and that it is all over now. I gaze at the plot of earth under which they placed her in a long, cheap box nearly three years ago now. One had so little money and death is so expensive! The *Valse bleue* flows and sings through all these thoughts like a leit-motiv that can summon her no more. I think of death's work underground. 'Poor Perruche!' I cannot help thinking every time: 'What a terrible state she must be in! The aqueous period, no doubt. When the parchment-like period supervenes, things will be better. But, in the meantime, it can't really be funny at all.'

Chapter 6

Mother of memories, queen of paramours . . .

BAUDELAIRE

I cannot deny that I have been lucky over this book: I saw my mother again a few months ago. I had then almost reached the end of Chapter 4, and in thinking of Chapter 5, was wondering what I could write to amuse the reader a little after all these tragic matters. When I saw my mother again, I had need to wonder no longer.

It was in October 1901, at my grandmother's in a northern town, that I had that pleasure. I had been summoned to attend the death-bed of a maiden aunt who was very ill, the aunt I mentioned on page 38. On the day I left, it occurred to me that I might once again meet that delightful woman, whom I had not seen for so long, come like myself to the dying woman's bedside. I was delighted at the prospect, but a little concerned too! When writing Chapter 3, I was thinking of my delicious mama of 1881; it was she I had known and wanted the reader to know. Who could tell what she would be like now? Would she be the withered, serious woman I so much feared to meet? I wondered whether I would be forced to regret having written about her as I had, and forced, also, to rewrite my chapter. For a moment, I almost decided not to go.

As soon as I arrived, my grandmother, whom I was now meeting for the first time, talked to me of my mother. I knew already that she was married, but I learned that she had two children, that she never spoke of me and, indeed,

never had spoken of me. Like me, she had been kept
informed of her sister's condition, and would certainly
come; but when? . . . I felt so embarrassed at the prospect
that I wondered whether to go away again. What would
she say when she found me there without warning?
'Nonsense,' said my grandmother, 'she won't recognise you.
It's so long since she saw you! At least twenty years, isn't
it? You'll see how young she still looks. One would never
think she had a grown-up son like you. It'll be all right,
you'll see.' And the fact is that those three days spent with
my mother were really delightful days.

She arrived on Thursday, 24th October, at about half-
past one, having been fifteen hours in the train. She had
come from Jean-Jacques Rousseau's country, where she
was then living, and had merely crossed Paris from one
station to another. It was after luncheon. I had been seeing
a visitor out and was just closing the door of the flat when
I heard steps and voices on the staircase. I opened the door
again and looked over the banisters. A woman was coming
up the stairs, dressed in black, carrying a little suitcase and
still speaking to the visitor going down. She had a pale,
clear-cut profile under very brown curls, a warm, musical
voice, and quick, supple movements. . . . I recognised her
at once. I went back into the flat, leaving the door ajar,
warned my grandmother and shut myself up on my room.
I can still remember how pale I looked in the mirror opposite
my bed.

She came in, kissed her mother, went and looked at her
sister, then came back to my grandmother's room to take
her things off and sit down. I could hear their voices from
my room. My grandmother's, slow and weary, my mother's
lively and impatient, uttering such words as these: my

husband, my children, my house, my maid. Then my mother wanted luncheon. Because the flat was so full we ate in the kitchen. To get there they had to pass through my room. My grandmother came in first, showing my mother, whose first visit to the flat it was, the way; then my mother followed. I was sitting on my bed and immediately got to my feet. My mother had not realised there was anyone there. She hesitated a moment, looked at me and said: 'How do you do, Monsieur!' She spoke in a rather low voice with a little inclination of the head. I replied: 'How do you do, Madame!' I spoke rather low too, and just as I would have done to any other woman. It took but a second and they had hardly left the room when I sat down on my bed again.

And now, so close at hand, in the kitchen with my grandmother, my mother was having luncheon, while my grandmother went to and fro serving her. My door had remained open and they were both talking in low voices. I soon heard my mother asking about the young man in the next room. 'Who is he?' she asked, lowering her voice. I immediately got to my feet and, purposely making a certain amount of noise, left my room to go and sit with the invalid at the other end of the flat. I did not want to hear my grandmother's answer. Half an hour went by, and then my mother went to unpack in my grandmother's room. I went to my grandmother and she said at once: 'I preferred not to tell her who you were. It might have embarrassed her. Later on, we shall see. I've said you're a friend from the theatre come to help us. . . .' How likely it was! A friend from the theatre, sleeping in the flat, going to and fro as if at home! And the nurse saying 'your nephew' to the invalid and I calling her 'Aunt'. It didn't make sense. My mother knew perfectly well who I was; my grandmother had told her straight away; she merely wanted it to appear as if she did not know. After all, as far as I was concerned, it made no difference. I might be very fond of her, but I had no intention of taking her by storm. As you may well suspect, I was not far wrong. When my aunt was dead and my mother had gone home to her husband and her children and her maid in Jean-Jacques Rousseau's country, my grandmother told me what had happened. When my mother had asked her: 'Who is that?' she had replied: 'It's Paul!' 'Who is Paul?' my mother had said. 'Why, your son, of course!' That had been all, and my mother had wanted to consider what line she should take. Should she make herself known to me, or remain a stranger? Oh, I know, you're astonished, you disapprove of her reserve, perhaps even blame her for it! Any other woman, you think, would have guessed it was her son at once and rushed to him, overcome with happiness. A paroxysm of joy, indeed! Blood calling to blood! I know all about that. But we do things differently in my family. We're a serious lot, we don't like flabbergasting people; besides we don't make emotional scenes suddenly like that, all about nothing. Life does not consist merely of high-flown sentiments!

I know too—for to be intelligent has its uses—that had I not acted in such a way as to make up her mind for her, she might well never have declared herself and, instead of talking to me as she did and as you will see later on, might have gone away again like a stranger. In face of all I know now, it seems to me practically certain. But what does it matter, since she did talk and I was able to kiss her! . . . Why am I not there still, on that Thursday, 24th October 1901, at about half-past ten at night, holding her in my arms? . . .

After a while, my mother came to find us and began talking to my grandmother in my presence. She spoke tenderly of her two children, her son and daughter. . . . Then my grandmother told me that Madame —— (for even to me she called her only by her Christian name or by her married name) would have to have my bed and that I must take a room in a nearby hotel. 'I must apologise, Monsieur, for making you turn out,' my mother said. 'Not at all, Madame. It's the least I can do,' I replied.

From that moment, the ice was broken, While my grandmother was busy about the flat, my mother asked me for news of Paris, of the Comédie, of people she used to know. I told her the news, really gossiped almost brilliantly, giving her my opinions, which would have gratified them, of the famous actresses, entertaining her with a whole heap of details and so on. But I could not help wondering, as I chattered, what she thought of me.

After dinner, when my grandmother had gone to bed to recover from all the nights she had sat up before our arrival, my mother and I went and sat in Fanny's room. The nurse and the little maid were there with us. My poor aunt, who died next day, was groaning continuously, her breathing already rather laboured. When my mother arrived, she had hardly recognised her. From time to time, she opened her huge staring eyes, at once bright and un-seeing, gazed out for a second and then relapsed into unconsciousness. Whenever her groaning grew louder, I got up, went to her, said, 'How do you feel, Aunt?' and took her hand; but it was mostly to see what my mother would do. Then my aunt would open her eyes as I have described, look at me, say a few words which were always the same: 'Oh, there you are!' And it was over till the next

93

time. My mother would have liked her sister to speak to her too. Each time I went over to the bed, she joined me there and spoke to her. 'Well, Fanny? Look, it's me! . . .' But she was always too late. Then she went back to her chair, brushing past me as if on purpose, and placing her hands on my shoulders as if to assist her in passing between the bed and the wall. She did this without embarrassment, as if we had known each other for many years. 'Would she really be so familiar if she did not know who I was?' I thought.

Towards eight o'clock, my aunt fell asleep and we each took an arm-chair to watch. The nurse and the little maid were both sitting at the end of the bed some distance from us, and talking to each other. My mother was sitting by the fireplace. The light from the lamp on the mantelpiece fell on her face, turning her complexion paler yet, her hair still more brown, and making her eyes, so full of a Jewish gentleness, still brighter. I was sitting not far from her by the window, half-covered in shawls, in a sort of faint shadow. How many memories revived in me as I watched this still desirable woman sitting so close to me! So this was my mother—the first woman I had known. How young she had remained! My grandmother was right. She would never have been taken for my mother. Moreover, I must admit that I do not think I could have loved a mother who had grown old. Several times, she told me to come nearer, closer to her. 'Why don't you draw your chair up?' she said; but I could not make up my mind to do so. 'It's very sweet of her,' I thought, pursuing my reflections. 'But if I'm really a stranger to her, it would hardly be proper for me to sit nearer to her, as if I were a husband or a son. Of course, in fact, she knows very well who I am, and so. . . .' And as she repeated her invitation, I got up, drew up my chair and sat down again. We were now so close to each other our knees touched.

Now that the light shone on my face, I dared not look at my mother. My elbows on my knees, I placed my head in my hands and sat there in silence, at once moved and indifferent, happy and embarrassed. I could feel my mother's eyes on me and could imagine what her thoughts must be. Above all, I appreciated the sadness of meeting again thus, a mother and a son, after two decades, she no longer young in years, and I a man. How we both sought for words! Two strangers could not have been harder put to it! Was it really so difficult to say to each other: 'Mama!' and: 'My son!'? I would have taken her so willingly in my arms! And I felt assailed by an immense discouragement, a great sloth at the thought of so many things to hear, so many things to say. 'After all, I have written the essentials,' I thought, thinking of the manuscript I had left in Paris. 'What does the rest matter? I would rather not have to make any alterations.' And the minutes went by, unused, adding silence to so much previous silence. Oh, the life we do not live! In their corner, the nurse and the little maid were still talking in low voices. They certainly did not suspect the close relationship between the lady and the young man sitting so close to each other and saying nothing! Even if they had been told, they would surely not have believed it. Outside, beyond the half-open window, were the wind, the freshness of the nearby sea, the cries of the local newspaper-boys and a whole assemblage of boring, provincial things. Yet I would have been happy to go out and look at them, so trying was the medicinal atmosphere of the room. At that moment, my aunt woke up and uttered a louder groan. I rose to my feet, went to her, took her hand and said from habit: 'How do you feel, Aunt? . . .' The nurse also got to her feet and fussed round her. I went and sat down again by my dear mama, who had not moved. Hardly had I sat down, when she said: 'Listen, Paul, I know who you are. . . .' And she told me many things in a low voice, things of long ago, things of her youth, of her first loves at the age of fifteen or sixteen. She talked to me of her childhood, of the life she had led since she had left me, of her husband and her children. My head in my hands, I sat listening to it all without pleasure. Everything she said embarrassed me, and I sought some means of making her stop. I told her I had no need to know all that. But she was launched and went on talking just the same. Moreover, she talked well! In an hour, she passed her whole life in review.

Leaning towards me like a sinner eager for absolution, she explained her many years' silence. She had often tried to find out what had happened to me, had questioned my grandmother and family, but always without result. She had seen my name in a newspaper two or three years ago linked with that of the *Mercure*. . . . Oh, if she had only known where to write! In 1900, she had come to Paris for the Exhibition with her husband and children; they had taken lodgings in the Rue Madame. How she would have rushed to see me had she only known where I lived! To think that we had been so near each other without knowing it. . . . But now we would make up for lost time. She did not have to conceal things. Her husband knew she had a grown-up son, for she had told him so at the beginning of their liaison, and had even led him to believe, from pride, that we wrote to each other regularly. . . . And she talked on thus, as if I were still a credulous child who listened without reflecting. The mysterious sea no doubt inspired her with these little deceptions! . . . But what was the good of taking her up on them? Is not a mother always right? Besides, everything she talked about so calmly, as if it had to do with another mother and another son, was so irreparable! I wanted merely to go to bed and not to have to think any more.

When she had more or less finished, she got up to go to bed, and I rose too, to accompany her. On reaching her room, what an embrace there was, as soon as the door was shut! 'My darling!' 'Mama!' What kisses! As I remember them, at this very moment of writing, I cannot help being so moved that I can scarcely put pen to paper. 'What a long time it has been!' I could not help saying in a low voice, my head on her shoulder, moved almost to tears. Alas, it had been so long a time, and to be embracing her was so new and even strange an experience that I behaved indelicately. Due partly, also, to my being accustomed to my darling tarts. . . . Unconsciously, I had put my arms round her waist, and was kissing her neck, her eyes, her throat. . . . Oh, if it were to do again, how I should do the same!

'A mother never changes,' she said, looking at me as I stood there, my hands in hers. 'Even though one hasn't seen one's son for a long time, one still loves him, is still ready to love him. . . . And you must write to me, you know, and call me "Mama". I'll give you my address and write to you, too. Poor Paul!' Then we kissed again. I was still behaving so indelicately that I could not help remarking on it.

'You mustn't mind, you know,' I said.

'Mind what?'

'I don't quite know, but I don't feel I'm really kissing you like a mother.'

'What do you mean?'

'I can't really put it into words. But I just feel it's not simply as a mother I kissed you.'

It seemed to me that her smile was one of slight embarrassment.

Then it was time to part, till next morning. She was going to bed and I to my hotel room. I can remember still the sensation of walking through the Rue de Guise and going up the hotel stairs in the dark. It had been so hard to leave her so soon, that I had tried to find some way of staying a little longer. 'You go to bed,' I said as she was turning down the sheets. 'I'll go into the sitting-room for a moment. I'll come back when you're in bed and sit by you a little.' But she had refused to allow it, though I insisted, and said gently: 'No, no.' And I had had to say a final goodnight and leave her. 'Why,' I wondered, 'does she not want me to see her and kiss her as I saw her and kissed her twenty years ago in that delicious room in the Passage Laferrière, as if I would not be even more sensible of it now that I am a man!' I think now that it must have been merely coquetry; perhaps she did not want me to see the traces of those twenty years upon her throat.

The next day, Friday, was a very busy day. When I arrived in the morning at about eight o'clock, I learned that my aunt had died about an hour earlier. She had been the one member of my family who was kind to me. In her eyes I had always remained a child, the slow and introspective little boy of long ago. 'Take care crossing the street, don't drink unboiled water, don't mix in public demonstrations, don't drink too much coffee, don't smoke too much, don't work too much at night, etc., etc.,' she wrote to me each week. And once a year she came to see me in Paris, took me out to dine in a *prix fixe*, which made me feel ill for three days afterwards, insisted on my making interminable journeys on the outsides of 'buses, the same journeys every year, carrying a multitude of parcels, and each year she told me the same stories, of which she was reminded by the houses we passed. In spite of the years, I had remained so tender-hearted that these well-meaning attentions did not bore me to excess. She had written to me barely a fortnight before and, so anxious was she not to worry me, had concealed the fact of her illness. When I arrived, my grandmother had invented a lie so that my presence should not be a shock to her. Oh, poor woman, how altered she was, and how much older she looked as she lay on her death-bed! I thought how lucky she was to have been but half-conscious throughout these last days. She would have been so saddened at the sight of my mother and me together after so long a time, for she had always thought that no good could come of our meeting. 'You know, it would be much better not to see her again, ever,' she said sometimes when I broached the subject on her visits to Paris. 'Your mother is relatively a much less serious person than you are. It would only make you sad.' But now she had no need to worry; whatever happened, she would never know. My heart disease might get worse from too many cigarettes and too much coffee; I might fall off an omnibus again, as had happened in 1898; I might overtire myself foolishly by trying to write masterpieces; my mother might even abandon me a second time; but she would not have to rush to my assistance and help me out of my difficulties. For a while, I gazed at her as she lay stretched out on the bed.

The nurse was putting a chin-bandage on her, and she now looked like a huge little girl, yellow, puffy and absurd. For all I could do, I felt my lip curl in a sort of mockery. Poor Fanny! I ought to have kissed her again for the last time. I wanted to. But I could not. None of it held any interest for me now, even though I had sung death's praises but a few months before in my writing.

I spent the morning running errands, then we had luncheon and then my mother and I began pouring out our hearts to each other again. I can still see myself sitting by her in my grandmother's room, between a chest of drawers and a little desk. We talked of so many things during the afternoon and evening of that day! If I tried to record them all I should never come to the end. A single word would often revive a dozen memories. It was different from our conversation of the day before in Fanny's room. Now, at least, we were talking of serious matters.

'Do you like women?' she asked suddenly, after a number of frivolous questions. Did I like women! To begin with, did I not love her? However, the question embarrassed me a little, and I behaved as if I had not quite understood what she meant. 'I mean, do you take pleasure in them,' she went on. 'Heavens,' I replied, feeling tenderness welling up inside me, 'of course, I think I love them very much even. But the pleasure they give me is perhaps a somewhat particular one. That is to say. . . .' 'Oh,' she interrupted, laughing at what she called my chastity, 'you are a funny boy!'

There was a silence, as if I were ruffled. She was playing with the châtelaine at her belt.

'You can't imagine,' I said, trying to change the conversation, 'the sort of way in which I've often thought of you, and it's very difficult for me to tell you.'

'Go on, tell me.'

'No, I wouldn't dare.'

'Why? What can it matter?'

'Oh, because it's very wrong; at least, you would think so. In any case, it can't be done.'

Nevertheless, to give her some idea of my memories, I reminded her of the day we had spent together in 1881 and in particular of my visit in the morning to the Passage Laferrière. 'Do you remember?' I asked her. 'Since that day, whenever I've thought of you, I've always seen you in that room, among your things, in bed and very *décolletée* Do you recollect? . . .' 'How very odd!' was all she found to say in reply. And we went on to talk of a whole lot of other things.

From time to time, I went to prowl secretly about her room, and pry into her belongings, that nothing of her personality might escape me. Until then, I had only moral memories of her, if I may use the term. But during these three days I spent with her, I increased my knowledge of her with many details. I know now that she takes size 4 in shoes, that her powder is Crimson Clover, that her toilet water comes from Houbigant, and that she uses tiny little hairpins, the sort called '*neigeuses*'. None of this seems important, I know; you may think it even of no interest. But when you find your mother again after twenty years, as I did, you think very differently, believe me, and the least fact delights you.

Between whiles, we kissed too, whenever we were alone or could hide behind a door. Oh, the dead woman lying there on the bed in the room at the end of the passage, a crucifix in her flaccid hands and candles all about her, could dream undisturbed! We had no thought of going to interrupt her. 'Kiss me quick, we're alone!' my mother would say, taking me by the neck with all the mischievousness of a child. And we kissed quickly and silently. 'All the same,' she said once, after our kisses, 'what would people think if they saw us kissing secretly like this!' And, another time, she said: 'You know, we look like two lovers even now. What would have happened ten years ago?'

Oh, but what did those ten years matter! She delighted me no less, this mother so much desired. I could not get over finding her as she was, so little changed, so slim and vivacious still, with her pale complexion and dark hair, curls down to her eyes, just as when she was thirty and I was ten and she had come to see me in that district of the Rue des Martyrs, which was so dear to me and full of women in her image. No, nothing had changed. Time had stood still. It was not true that I had become so loved of women and had acquired so many memories at such little cost. I had found the same mama as in the past and, when she kissed me, it was the child I had been that stirred in me, and I would have liked to become him once again to be able to snuggle more closely in her arms. Indeed, I was so happy at finding her unchanged that, finally, I had to admit my pleasure. 'I really didn't expect to see you as you are,' I said at a moment when she was allowing me to gaze at her. She didn't quite understand what I meant. 'How's that?' she said. 'Yes,' I went on, 'I thought of you as being stout, grave and severe, a real bourgeoise in fact!' She uttered a delicious, hoydenish laugh that I can still hear as if she were standing before me. 'You delight me,' I added. 'You don't look as if you were married. I like you best like that.'

She usually called me Paul but, from time to time, when

we were alone together, she would call me her child and, also, her darling. How touched I was! As when the dearest of my friends calls me her precious. I would turn my head away for a moment the better to savour, as if I were alone, the sweetness of these charming little endearments. If only I could have been her child again in reality. For then, my arms about her neck and my face in her bosom, she would have kissed me as I used to like being kissed. To think that it was over and done with, that it was now too late! As she was to write to me later on, she had not seen me grow up, and had suddenly found me a man. And I had seen her so little, in all about the equivalent of five or six days when I was a child. And because of it, there was a certain sensual excitement in our relations, fluttering from her to me, and from me to her. Oh, from me to her, above all! 'My darling Jeanne!' I called her in my heart. And I thought, as I already began to feel it, of the emotion I should sustain in embracing her, my mother, as a mistress! After all, she was a woman like another. And she had seen me so little as a child. For her, I must be merely a man, and a young man at that! Besides, since I was her son, perhaps I could not be altogether displeasing to her? . . . To what intimate physical details my thoughts strayed. . . . Yes, to her whole body. . . . And what was she thinking as she looked at me? . . . Had she the same sense of a double tenderness as I, a sensual emotion made up at once of family feeling and physical desire? Who could tell? Loose as she had been and still seemed to be considering the questions she had asked. . . . Oh, to take her in my arms and, her head on my shoulder, to cover her with kisses, weeping like a child perhaps, that was what I wanted above all! But, as if it were fated, I was being continually interrupted. When it was not my shyness that gained the upper hand, someone came, my grand-mother, the maid, or an undertaker's employee—with what an air of melancholy!—to ask for instructions or take measurements. Or, suddenly, my mother went into another room. And then I had to begin things all over again! Besides, I thought it over to excess. I weighed the pros and cons too much. For instance, she had told me to address her in the second person and call her mama, when we were alone; yet, despite the pleasure it would have given me, I did not do so. I felt that if I addressed her so familiarly I should end by saying things that were too ardent and that, after all, was perhaps better avoided. . . . Nevertheless, I dared to say *tu* to her on one occasion. It was the evening of the same day. I was about to leave her to go to bed and return to my hotel room. She had come with me to the door and we were standing on the threshold in the dark. 'No,' I said to her in a low voice, as she kissed me before I started down the dark stairs, 'no, in spite of all I could say, you'd never know how much I loved you!'

Amid these pleasures, however, I never ceased thinking about my book in Paris. Ever since my mother had arrived and we had begun loving each other so madly, I had been taking as many notes as I could. On one occasion, she actually saw me doing it. 'What are you up to, continually taking papers from your pocket and going off to write in corners?' she asked. I got out of it only by telling her I was keeping an account of my expenses as I went along.

But sometimes, too, the discouragement, the sloth from which I had suffered the first evening came over me again. Particularly at night, when I had gone back to the Hôtel du Sauvage, towards midnight, and began thinking about the whole story, alone in my fireless room: an anonymous room with impersonal furniture, where there was nothing familiar to welcome one, not even the shadowy silence. How alone I felt, in spite of my critical sense! I thought, trying to make a joke of it, that my mother's tenderness was of no great account, that it would pass soon enough. There were conventional phrases in everything she said. . . . And I immediately reproved myself. 'After all,' I thought, 'she is doing the best she can, the dear woman. One must not ask too much of her. It's already a great deal to have seen her again. Is it her fault if life for both of us has turned out as it has?' Then I would take my notebook, on which this chapter is based, and keep it up to date by transcribing the day's notes into it. They already filled five or six pages! I had almost another chapter for my book! And, good heavens, it might well be the most luminous of all my emotional relationships! Grandeur of the man of letters! One may be a son, one may have found one's mother again after twenty years of separation, the moment one has a book on the stocks, it takes precedence over everything. One cannot feel, hear or see anything without wanting to put it into the book, however sacred it may be. But it may be that these things were not very sacred. . . .

The next day, Saturday, my aunt's funeral took place. There was only a service in the church, for the burial was to take place in Paris. I took charge of the funeral; on the announcement, my mother had put my name right at the bottom, after those of her two children. What a thing to do, when I come to think of it! For not one moment, from the removal of the body to the sealing of the van at the station, did I think of the dead woman. My thoughts were wholly concerned with my mother. Even in the church, I kept turning round to look at her as she knelt on her prie-dieu, and her thoughts seemed elsewhere too. I remember that as we were coming back from the station I made a woman turn round because I was chanting a passage from the burial service as I walked along. Yet I was very fond of my aunt, the service was not bad and I'm not insensible to church music! But I was so infatuated with my mother during those days. . . . In compensation, I sometimes dream of poor Fanny now; I see her cured and taking me once again to nasty restaurants.

When it was over, we returned to the house. I was leaving that evening at six o'clock to take my aunt's body to Paris. It was the last day I spent with my mother. Only a few hours more, and I would be leaving this woman who was so dear to me, and this town in which I had had the joy of seeing her again. How little of all the things I had to say to her had I said and how I suffered at having to leave! Would I ever see her again? She herself was leaving the next day. We were to meet in the evening at the Gare du Nord, dine, and be together till the train left to take her back to her country of chalets. Two or three hours to spend in a café, in a cab and in a station crowded with people and luggage!

We had luncheon, and my mother and I went for a stroll in the town, to recover a little from the atmosphere of death and its trappings, and all the guests who looked like the sort of characters who appear in the last act of a play. How good it was to stretch our legs and take the air in the wide avenue! Oh, the way my mother walked in those high-heeled boots she was still accustomed to wear! She chattered as we went along, people stared at us a little—it was a provincial town, don't forget—and I was so concerned with my own feelings that I made mistakes in answering her.

Why did I have to be walking with her in this town rather than in Paris, in my favourite district of the Rue des Martyrs, where the smallest detail would have filled us with a tender delight? Being so close to leaving her, I was shyer than ever. I needed the intimacy of a closed room with deep chairs where memories are more secret.

How sad the time was between our return to the house and my departure! It would have been altogether too painful but for the fact that we did up some parcels together. My mother gave me a few little presents, an old card-case she had had when young, and had found in a drawer, a little sweet-box, a photograph of her son and a piece of soap. We talked a little of this and that, of things of no importance; she remarked, for instance, that I had small hands and feet; and she thought, too, that I was not dressed smartly enough. We agreed about our meeting the next day. 'I shan't do you justice in this horrible dress,' she remarked because of her mourning. Then, when we were alone, she said: 'Tomorrow, you know, we must *tutoyer* each other and you must call me mama.' But even these kindnesses could not console me. Indeed, at about four o'clock, my depression increased. 'You are in the dumps!' she said, coming to me and putting her arm round my neck. 'Oh,' I replied, 'I almost regret having seen you. At least, before. . . .'

Then it was nearly dinner-time. We were alone. I wrote down the times of her trains, our meeting-place and my address, as she had asked me. 'Right,' I said, 'it's agreed then: tomorrow, at the Gare du Nord, at six o'clock?' And I added: 'Unless you've changed your mind. . . .' She looked at me. 'Unless,' I went on, 'you'd prefer not to see me again. . . .' She made no reply and looked put out and unhappy. Why had I said that, when all I wanted was to please and mollify her? 'You won't be as horrid as that tomorrow, will you?' she said, taking me in her arms and kissing me. How moved I was at that moment, my face against her breast, clasped by those hands which had never rocked me to sleep! Almost in tears, I said I was sorry, and I kissed her too, perhaps rather more than was proper. But what did I care for the proprieties when she was tender towards me?

The time to go arrived in the middle of dinner and I got up to get my things ready. My mother remained at the table. I had been able to say no more than, 'Goodbye, Madame,' because of the little maid. She came and joined me and helped me pack, but without a word. She merely said at the last moment: 'Don't forget anything, will you?' And I should certainly have left her thus, if I had not taken the initiative and kissed her. It was only when I had already gone, that I realised I had left my hat behind. I came back. My mother had already gone to her room. She did not appear. Could she possibly have gone to bed already in order to be able to think of me the sooner?

What a journey it was! From six o'clock in the evening till five next morning in a slow train, my aunt's body travelling quietly behind me in its own van! Every time I go by train, I always think I'm starting on that journey again. It was really time I returned to Paris and recovered my usual habits and way of life. I could already see in imagination the pure column of unpolished crystal, the fountain in the Luxembourg gardens, raised in the twilight. I was thinking also of my book, which was so behindhand. There was no doubt that as a result of all these events it would be at least a month before I could get to work again.

And my pretty friends to whom I hadn't even written a line! Dear creatures, perhaps I should find they had become mothers or were about to become so? And what a compensation that would be! Alone, in my compartment, I kept repeating that sweet word 'mama', which I had for so long dreamed of saying to that dear, neglectful woman. Little unknown towns flickering past in the night, great industrial centres with their quietly smoking chimneys, the day's work done, bracing seaside resorts with a glimpse of a glimmering sea, plains flecked with marshes, clumps of trees and the ribbons of roads, Boulogne, Étaples, Noyelles, Saint-Valéry, Abbeville and the rest, what a bore they all were! Fragments of Peer Gynt ran softly through my head. I was also distinguishing between my feelings of melancholy and the sorrows of love. At least, an ordinary lover, if he has read a little, can always console himself by reciting verses from some poet or other. Under the influence of words, he becomes less distraught. But no one has written verses about the sadness of being abandoned by one's mother. Search as I might, I could think of none.

How impatiently I looked for the outline of the Sacré-Coeur.

I shall say nothing of my arrival in Paris, nor of my waiting for the van from the undertaker's till nine o'clock in a little café opposite the station, where I drank a variety of things. There was a whole crowd of prostitutes and pimps! These details are to be avoided. By ten o'clock it was all over: my aunt was in her tomb and I was at home. I had nothing to do but await the hour for my meeting with my mother. I could not sit still. At about half past four, I went out. How alive I felt! And though as a rule I looked at them with such delight, how cold the women I saw from the cab left me! The woman I was going to meet was worth the lot of them, and I was ready to follow her, if she so wished. No doubt, we were only to dine together! But suppose she suddenly took it into her head to take me along with her? One must be ready for anything where a mother is concerned. At my grandmother's she had been embarrassed. But now that we were to be alone. . . . Just before reaching the station, I went into a florist's and bought some flowers, not quite knowing how I would manage to give them to my mother. But the pale violets would look so well against her mourning. Besides, I did not care if I was indelicate. . . .

I reached the station at five o'clock. There was an hour to wait. I walked up and down the platform, reading the notices: THE PUBLIC IS REQUESTED . . . THE PUBLIC IS INFORMED . . . IT IS FORBIDDEN . . . I carried my flowers in my hand, and every now and then sat down on a barrow. And thus I waited till eight o'clock for trains on which my mother never was. Everything was against me: the trains were late, the railway officials knew nothing. Oh, those officials, with what bad grace they gave me information! No doubt, *they* had their mothers at home! In the end, I put the violets in my pocket and little by little they withered under their gay paper, which quickly creased, while the idea I had conceived of this meeting gradually faded away. I no longer knew what to think. Either my mother had not left or she had arrived without my seeing her. But could she possibly have passed me without my seeing her, or without her seeing me? Not unless she had done it on purpose. . . . But why? Surely, she could not have left and there must be a wire for me at home.

I left the station and took a cab. There was no wire at

home. I went to the Gare de Lyon. It was eight thirty-five when I got there. My mother's train was due to leave at eight fifty. I went to the platform, enquired which train it was and ran for it. . . . Alas, it is so true that one must never hurry, however lively one's desire, or great the object of it, so true that wisdom is to tarry at the risk of missing everything. Yet I knew it well. Pascal and Beaumarchais had taught it me: 'To possess is but little, it is to enjoy that makes one happy. . . .'—and life happy too, and I should have remembered it better. My darling mama was there, leaning out of the compartment window, with a calm air of waiting to see if, by any chance, her good young son would come. 'Well, my boy, what's the matter?' she said, as I came up and got into the compartment, which she had to herself. What was the matter, indeed? And you can guess how our conversation went. Our conversation! I exaggerate! Face to face with this woman, whom I loved better than anyone else in the world and whom I was on the point of losing once more, I could do nothing but burst into tears. It was absurd, I know, in a big fellow like me! Fortunately, my mother kept her countenance. Had she not, she would have laughed so much the guard would have come to see what the matter was. She talked of the whole thing quite calmly, as if it were of no importance! After all, it was only an appointment missed! As if our meetings were as numerous as all that! Then, she sat down. She was clearly exhausted. 'Poor boy,' she said, 'everything'll be all right. We shall meet again. We'll make up for it.' Then she kissed me, just once—I counted it—and remarked that there were a lot of people from her town about, who knew her. I was particularly touched by this. In any case, they were beginning to slam the doors. I put my violets on the seat beside her, said goodbye and left. Oh, I had no need of poets' verses now! None of them could weep, as my love, my thoughts and my memories wept. To have grown up alone, brought up by strangers. . . . Having promised myself so often to gain her affection should I ever find her again through the years. . . . Incorrigible idiot, try to be less idiotic in future!

I was thinking these things and many others, as I went home on foot through the horrible district of the Gare de Lyon. I would have liked to go and finish the evening in some Folies-Bergère or other. There, I should find affectionate women, or at least women who knew how to simulate affection. Brilliant scenes, which sometimes quiver as does my heart! But it was so late.

I crossed the wooden bridge where I used to go nearly every Sunday to sit and talk with Valéry before he married.

I would willingly have given sixpence to have been an orphan from birth.

Chapter 7

Je t'aimais inconstant, qu'eussé-je fait, fidèle!

RACINE

I am thinking quietly of what the reader is probably saying to himself at this point: 'The train has left for Switzerland. The young man has gone home and needs consoling. He's going to stop prattling about his dear mama and we're going to see him with his women friends again.' The reader is rather too impatient.

The day after this very odd evening—I, nevertheless, owe to it the sentences on the previous page or so, which seem to me not too bad—I wrote my mother a letter which was at once emotional yet mocking, tender yet disabused etc.; for the first time, I wanted to make an impression. 'Am I right or wrong to write to you?' I said, when I had reproached her a little for the excessive propriety of her behaviour the day before. 'I thought for quite a while before beginning this letter. It seemed to me that if I wrote I might perhaps annoy you, for I cannot write without tenderness; if I did not, you would hold it against me and accuse me of indifference. So I decided to write you a line or two.' By the time I had signed my name, I had written six pages.

The most touching part of the whole business was that my mother wrote to me the same day, just a line in haste, as she said, to assure me of her affection. As if that were necessary! 'My dearly loved son, why should such a tiresome mischance have deprived me of the delightful hours I

113

was looking forward to spending with you ? . . . Write to me
at length, treat me as a friend, love me, your place was all
ready in my heart. . . . Thank you for the flowers, what a
charming thought! And how touched I was! . . . My dear
boy, receive the tender kisses of your mother who has never
forgotten you and to whom your presence has been like a
ray of sunlight in the heart.' She must read terribly bad
books, I thought, as I read the last phrase over again.

I replied the following day, and a considerable correspondence began between us. 'You must not mind the
way I behaved on Sunday,' my mother wrote in her second
letter. 'You must remember I was surrounded with people
I knew, that you are a man and that I do not look my age. . . .
I have forgotten how to let myself go, for I am not the happy
woman you think me. . . . My kisses were embarrassed, you
say; but, I repeat, you are a man and I did not watch you
grow up. . . . There are so many things, you silly boy, one
has to be careful about! . . .' And now she was being sorry
for herself! 'I find difficulty in believing you are not happy,'
I said in my reply. 'You have a good husband and two
children whom you love; and, what's more, you've suddenly
found a sentimental grown-up son who writes you letters of
six pages without a blush. If that isn't happiness, what more
do you want ?'

Yes, it was quite a correspondence. My mother wrote to
me and I wrote to her, she replied and I replied, and it
lasted as long as it could—that is to say, not long. But what
does that matter! Through these letters we were able to
show each other the sort of mother and son we were.
Besides, what a mother! The fourth time she wrote to me,
she sent me back half the bunch of violets I had given her
at the station. 'I have kept it as a token of remembrance,'

she said. 'And I am sharing it with you, my darling, to prove to you once and for all that you are very close to my heart.' I quote at random from her other letters: 'Oh, let nothing destroy our delightful romance of love, my dear son! . . . After luncheon I sometimes lie on my *chaise-longue* and pretend to be asleep and think, of whom ? You can guess it's of you, whom I hope to see again soon . . . I dream all sorts of things . . . I see you here; of going to see you as often as possible and bringing you secretly home. . . . At other times, it's in Paris, in your flat, where we can see each other and kiss as much as we like. . . . But these are all dreams and, sad or gay, they all have the same object. . . . But my imagination runs so wild at times that I have great difficulty in controlling it, not that I bear it any grudge for that. . . . However artificial a happiness it gives me, it is happiness nevertheless. . . . When shall we be able to spend a day together ? . . . I should so much like to talk to you other than by letter to ask you a whole heap of things that are too difficult to write! . . . This may happen sooner than you think, and I shall try to be your pretty mama once more, you vain flatterer whom I love so much. . . .' I have forgotten her mother's heart, of which she also wrote a good deal.

'Your letters and the flowers you sent me,' I wrote on my side, doing my best to live up to the tone of her letters, 'gave me such pleasure as you cannot imagine. . . . When I think of you for rather too long, it seems to me my thoughts become troubled a little. . . . No, you can't possibly know how much. . . . I imagine you nearer to me and you are at once my dear mama and an adorable creature. . . . Oh, if you were with me at those moments! . . . Yet, who knows, perhaps I'd say nothing, as at my grandmother's when I was

so shy? . . . You don't hold it against me, do you? . . .
Women never like men to be shy! . . . If you knew how I
have thought of you for the last ten years. . . . Do you ever
think of me? When you lean over your son to kiss him or
scold him, do you ever think of that other son, whom you
recovered by chance, for he loves you both as a child and as
a man, more as a man, perhaps! . . . Oh, and this morning
there was the same mist as during those few days in October
when we were together! . . . Do you remember the evening
of the day of your arrival, in your room, when I asked you
to get into bed and to let me come back for a little? . . . You
refused, hiding yourself ill-naturedly from me as from a
child who does not know what a woman is. . . . Would you
allow me to one day, now that you know how much I love
you? . . . I know very well that you're going to lecture me
again. . . . Really, it's not all that fun, you know, thinking
I shall see you only at more or less distant intervals, almost
in passing, as a traveller barely arrived feels already the
melancholy of packing and departing. If I could only see you
at once! But what would our relations be? Would you still
be my pretty mama of 1881, whom I'm still crazy about,
and would I be still more embarrassed yet?'

It was on these lines I wrote to her, two or three times
a week, never in the same words, but always with the same
ardour. From time to time, I gave vent to light reproaches
and suspicions, anxious about some detail, distressed by
some delay. When I think of it now, I tell myself it is
probably a good thing it's all over between us. The thought
of that woman was with me always. I could spend hours at
a time thinking of her, of the circumstances of her life, of
our unexpected meeting so full of constraint, of her living
far away with a husband and two children. No, it was not

life alone that had separated us, nor had anyone done anything to prevent our seeing each other again, as she asserted.
For all that she was able to contrive a thousand tender
phrases, one does not become fond so suddenly, and in her
heart of hearts she can never have cared for me. So many
years had gone by since she had abandoned her little son!
There was a good deal of excuse for her. . . . I can say now
that I did my best to analyse our relationship. Each of her
letters, though they made me so happy, was nevertheless
an opportunity for ratiocination. Her charming phrases, in
which at times there was even a certain coquetry, to put it
no higher than that, her caressing words that aroused
memories of my childhood, were all, I told myself, no more
on her side than a minor expression of pity, a sort of duty,
a kind of compensation she wished to give me. 'Corresponding with you is really rather difficult owing to the
deplorable habit you have of reading things that aren't
there between the lines,' she wrote to me on one occasion,
when things were beginning to go less well. The fact was
that everything she had told me at my grandmother's
during that extraordinary evening of confidences, and
everything she wrote to me now, when she felt the need
to explain matters, were so unlikely! It was much more
probable that I would never have seen her again if I had
not gone to Fanny; that her husband, far from believing
that we were corresponding, must wish us never to meet
again; and that she very likely had to read my letters and
write to me in secret. Moreover, I had proof of it in what
my grandmother had said: 'Jeanne has never mentioned
you to us,' and in what my mother had written to her as
soon as she had reached home (my grandmother, that
excellent woman, had shown me the letter): 'You can write

of Paul in your letters. My husband has read the funeral announcement and I have told him Paul is a nephew of Fanny's.' And, indeed, her lies seemed to be tending to increase rather than diminish! . . . But could it really be so? Could time efface even the maternal instinct? Could these letters I read and reread be dictated merely by compassion and necessity, with the idea, so to speak, of gaining time? . . . What she wrote was sometimes so tender, appeared so true, seemed to rise from the depths of a heart that had been regretfully silent for so many years! . . . Oh, the truth, of which I was certain, of which I took pleasure in being certain—and which I yet forced myself not to recognise! Once, my mother finished her letter with the word *adieu*, a word they use in those parts, so it seems, as we here say *au revoir*, without its implying any idea of separation. Not knowing it, I was more anxious than ever. I was so fearful of losing her again, and felt so certain I should lose her! 'Never *adieu*,' I wrote to her, 'even to the end. If I were only twenty, if I were only ten, it would add ten years, twenty years to my age!'

As I write this chapter, I have the whole correspondence before me: my mother's letters on the one hand, and copies of my own on the other. What lively, searching things both sides of this correspondence contain, even the last letters, though they are a little too seemly! What darlings, adored mothers, sweet idiots, dearest womans, hearts full of love and passages full of memories they contain! They will really make several admirable pages in a few years' time, if there is no means of using them before then. I first thought of reproducing them in this book to save the trouble of copying out quotations, which I have done in a hurry and perhaps rather badly; but then I had second thoughts, indeed scruples: for a published price of three francs, this book contains enough—and I have remitted the letters to a later date. It will be better, too, that a little time should elapse. Between now and then I may have acquired a little talent and a taste for fine phrases, which now seem to me so difficult; my capricious darling will probably be dead; I shall then be able to write of our love as it should be written of, and without appearing to make a scene. Besides, having by then written so much, for I hope I shall be given numerous commissions, I shall end by having no more subjects to write about and be delighted to find these letters again. I can already imagine the charming preface to the book, which of all my books will have cost me the least pains—yet, I wonder! And I shall write it, having retired out of circulation, among a few, charming friends on the shady side of forty! To assert that it will be entirely suitable for young ladies would perhaps be an exaggeration; but it will make me a little money anyway. I have so many bouquets to give my mother! And that will be the moment!

There are, however, two of these letters which might have found a place here, as a little supplement to Chapter 3. It was about half way through our correspondence that my mother wrote them. She had seen that poetic little work I published together with my great friend Van Bever, in 1900, lying about at my grandmother's, and had thereby discovered that I wrote. Whether she was flattered at the thought, I cannot tell, but as soon as she got home, she wrote to ask me to send her a copy of the book. On a handsome postcard, illustrated with her photograph, she wrote: 'My dear Paul, will you please tell my mother to bring your volume of poetry with her. I have not been able to read it with a sufficiently quiet mind to appreciate it as it deserves I am sure.' We were so busy loving each other! You can say what you like, there are good moments in life! Without really knowing why, I had not at once fulfilled her wishes, but then, one day, without warning her, I sent her the book, enclosing in it, as if by mistake, two or three of those *Essais* I had written in moments of inspiration for the *Mercure*. If the truth be told, this was not altogether disinterested. A few days before, I had displeased my mother by some over-emotional phrases in one of my letters and she had made a considerable fuss about it: 'I must admit,' she had written, 'that I am often disquieted by the nature of the affection you manifest. Your correspondence, which was such a pleasure to me to keep, is sometimes so equivocal that it might be dangerous and I shall therefore destroy it, I think. . . . If you are reasonable, you will send me back all my letters' (did she think them equivocal too?) 'and our correspondence will date only from this letter. . . .' Yes, indeed, letters about the weather, I thought, exactly what letters between a mother and son should be; and I had not been reasonable, I had contented myself with writing to her and patching things up; she had not insisted; and sending her my writings after such amiability seemed to me an excellent means of showing myself more amiable still, while waiting to begin all over again.

She was delighted and told me so in such warm terms that I thought, as I read her letter: 'I've found a public at last, and it's none too soon!' 'What pleasure reading your works gave me,' she wrote, 'and how I wish there were more of them.' Was she also going to reproach me with my lack of energy? Oh, mothers! . . . But the odd thing was that she went on: 'What talent you have for writing!'

(A little attempt at irony, perhaps?) 'If I were you, I should make a novel of my life. It's a fertile subject and, properly treated, you could make your fortune by that alone. Have you never thought of it?'

For all that people who know me maintain there was nothing very startling about this, I persist in thinking it was odd at least that my mother should write to me of the book I was actually in process of writing, without knowing anything about it. A novel about my life! And I who had always thought that life was not a novel, but merely clownish! Clearly, we were mother and son. We did not know each other very well it is true; indeed, we were more or less strangers. Nevertheless, we both had the same idea; I a little earlier, she a little later, that's all. It was so touching, I felt myself become quite filial.

I wrote to her: 'Did you mention my writing a sort of novel of my life just casually, or had you thought about it seriously? . . . What things I could tell you about it, if I did not fear you would become severe with me again. Nevertheless, have you really thought carefully about it? The little I have let you see in my letters of my way of loving you has resulted only in your making a fuss. What would happen, and what would you think, if I published a book in which I was frank about my emotions, concerned merely to be sincere and please myself? Of course, we alone would know the true story and that you are my mother and I your son! Nevertheless, what would you say? Please don't answer at once; keep it for another day. You were bound to start talking to me about my writing when even my best friend never knows anything about it! On the few occasions anyone has talked to me about what I'm doing, I've never been able to help bursting out laughing.

In the end I shall do the same by you, you know. Better not, don't you think?'

She did not, however, keep it for another day. 'It was not lightly that I wrote about a novel of your life,' she replied at once. 'And if I understand rightly you have either thought of it or even perhaps begun it. *Whatever it may contain*' (they are her italics), '*I shall not be angry, you can be sure of that.* I would much rather answer you at once for I shall not change my mind; and, besides, as you say, no one will recognise me in Paris, where everyone has forgotten me, and here, at ———, no one could possibly suspect me. . . . Write to me on this subject, which interests me very much, and whatever you want to say, say it, come what may, both in your letters and in your novel, if you do decide to do it, which I advise. Just think! No need for any imaginative effort, just let your pen run on and write a history! And then, you know, even if you have to say a few hard things about me, don't worry, I shan't be angry. In any case, my anger never lasts long. I shall discharge the debt by lecturing you, if it's really necessary. . . . When one goes to confession, one tells everything, is absolved—and begins again! You will do the same, and so shall I!'

Wasn't I right in saying that my mother was adorable! And now I could do no other than tell her the facts, that is to say that I was indeed writing a book very similar to the one she was advising me to write. And that was what I did, quite shortly, of course, and limiting myself to telling her about the chapter on my childhood; as for the rest, she would see it quite soon enough, I thought. It suited me all the better owing to the fact that, since we had met again, I had remembered a whole heap of things about my childhood and feared there would be lacunae in my chapter, particularly about the number of times we had seen each other. I did not want to begin it all over again, which would have been a bore, nor make changes, which would have wrecked it. But if my mother were willing to help me, if she would write her recollections for me! What a wonderful collaboration it would be! There would be a little more of her in the book; I would have the advantage of a few more pages for further chapters; and what pages there would be about me too! I wrote to her at once, giving her a plan, explaining what I wanted, etc. How much I would have preferred to have this—I flatter myself—unique mother beside me, that I might read to her the pages she will now perhaps never see, while adroitly skipping the passages that needed skipping.

After a few days, having thought and searched her memory, as she said, she replied with two long letters, each of eight pages, which however told me little that was new, and this has decided me to leave these letters with the others. How many adorable and touching details these two letters contained, however, and what pleasure they gave me, as my mother so kindly described for me those delicious years between 1874 and 1882, dates I can never read or write without emotion! It seemed to me that I could see from afar all those charming memories of my childhood and her youth reflected on her features, as they had shone in my mind during the hours I was writing of them. Oh, what luck for a mother to have a son like me, a son who writes his memoirs while still a young man! And yet, how trying she must have found it to look back through all the years to a more amiable and gracious time, to the little boy who was so little trouble and the rarely pretty mama she had been. Those were good times, times of coquetry, freedom and wantonness. One went to see one's son between two journeys, for ten minutes or for a day, then one went off again to enjoy oneself, having indulged one's affection. What a pleasure to remember it all, without effort, since one's writer son had made a little guide for one—now that one was a serious woman, or nearly so! Yet she succeeded so well in helping me to write my book, that she wrote almost better than I. The most obliged of the two of us was perhaps her son.

Nevertheless, I had done well to hurry, as you will see.

I wrote to her for New Year's Day to wish her a happy New Year for the first time in my life. 'How late to begin these charming compliments,' I thought. Had I listened to my heart, I would have bought a big sheet of flowered paper such as those on which I used to send my good wishes as a child. Once again, she had written at the same time as I and, next day, I received her letter filled with a thousand endearments. Really, what with two letters about my book, two other letters of reminiscences, and now a New Year's letter! . . . Had she ceased being angry about my letters? But a few days later she wrote me another long letter in which, so she said, she wished to talk to me seriously. Seriously? . . . I lay comfortably back in my chair to read it. Oh, there were no 'my darlings', in this one, no bouquet preceded nor was to follow. And it was a bit hot, as one says: '. . . And so, my dear Paul, in accordance with a decision which I shall not alter,' my mother wrote, 'I ask you to send me back all my letters, including this one . . . I have already destroyed all yours; our correspondence can begin again as soon as I receive them, affectionate and tender on my side and, on yours, calmer I hope. Don't ask me if you can keep them, it will be useless, I want them all. . . .'

What was I to do, grow angry, take the same tone? Never on your life! It was better to answer without answering, explain myself as best I could, try to patch things up once more. . . . Perhaps my mother would get off her high-horse in the end! . . . I might have saved myself the trouble, since my mother's only answer was to copy, more or less, her preceding letter. She knew how to avoid over-tiring herself, as you can see! I let a few days go by, and then, the day after my birthday, without saying a word about her letters, I wrote to tell her I had been born thirty years ago the day before. 'How far away it all is, isn't it?' I said. I had written first: 'How old it makes one feel . . .' but then had begun again, so as not to sadden, even ever so slightly, the fantastic creature who was so dear to me in spite of everything. Ten days elapsed; then she replied with a letter in which she called me *vous*, as if writing to a lover with whom she was preparing to break things off, and which was signed only with an initial. 'You very well know the reason for my silence. So long as you do not send me back my letters, every single one of them, I shall no longer write to you, and this is the last warning I shall give you. . . .' (Tender-hearted people may be reassured: my mother was exaggerating and was still to write to me sometimes.) But she said not one word about my birthday, about the birth of the little boy of long ago. Did it mean nothing to her, then? *Mother of memories*. . . . Ah, that's what you think!

And now it was goodbye to the phrases by which one gains time, by which, when lucky, one moves people, by which, sometimes indeed, one can make oneself loved. I had to make up my mind, and reply, and send these letters from a mother back; they were all I had of her, all I ever would have. . . . Except, I suppose, the life she had given me! But to hell with that! For two or three nights I considered the matter, with the letters lying before me as if I were an archivist, and I smiled, I may say, with a smile I reserve for my great days. After all, since it had to be! And I refused. . . .

I still don't regret this reply today, or rather I don't care a rap any more. And yet, when I think of its consequences. . . . Charming sentiments were destroyed in me for ever. My mother wrote me one more letter, without mentioning my name in it anywhere, and again signed it with only an initial. 'After this letter,' she said, 'you will never hear from me again.' I was beginning not to care; I no longer had the heart; things must go as they must; and I replied with only a few words: '. . . What a pity—don't you feel it?—to see days of life spoilt thus!' I ended in a rather literary way. 'However, let's think no more about it. "Farewell, we must part!" as the English song has it. Perhaps we shall begin again one day!'

A month, perhaps less, perhaps more—I feel too lazy to search through the letters to make sure—went by, when one fine day my mother—shall I ever know why?—invented things, made accusations. . . . Against me, who for ten years had known where to write to her, but had never done so, since I thought I had no right to disturb her oblivion! It really did not encourage one to be a good son! 'I regret but one thing,' she wrote in the same letter, 'and that is to have given you in my letters, and out of duty, the illusion of an affection I could not feel, since I did not know you. . . .' Oh, so then it was true I was a psychologist, since from the very first day. . . . Anyway, there it was! From now on, psychology would be my strong point, and, to begin with, I wrote my mother a letter, and what a letter! I passed in review everything she had told me, everything she had written me since we had met again, ransacking everything, analysing everything. Oh, what talent I displayed in that letter! My pen couldn't travel fast enough; there were tears in my eyes and I was laughing at the same time; and what I wrote was very like me. I would have done better to spend that day in bed. My letter was hardly in the post when I regretted it. I could have gone into the post office and asked for it back at once, I know. But I can never make up my mind on the spur of the moment. I always have to consider the pros and cons of the least thing for several hours, and it was only after luncheon that I made up my mind to try to get my letter back. I spent the whole afternoon of that Easter Monday, 31st March 1902, running from post office to post office and to the General Post Office, to demand that my letter be stopped. I shall remember that day for a long time. But it was the holiday period, many of the employees were away; it was all quite useless, and my mother received the letter. In spite of my serious tone, it's really no use my mocking: it's just possible I failed in my duty as a son that day.

If only my mother had not replied! But four days later her reply came, a fat letter with two seals! I was working hard and had no time for amusement. I gave the letter to a trustworthy friend to see if I dared risk reading it. I was assured I had better not, that with my tender sensibilities it might induce me to write of melancholy things in this book, etc. And so I left the heavily sealed letter on one side. . . . I have not opened it yet. There it is, in my drawer, with the town's postmark: ———, and the date: 4th

April 1902. I shall open it later on, when I publish the others; I shall therefore have a surprise for an epilogue. Or perhaps I shall never open it. . . . What does it matter: now, later, or never? Sometimes in the evenings, when I'm clowning among my memories, I take it out, put it on the table in front of me and, my head in my hands, weep over it silently in my heart. How I should like to be able to weep properly! Sometimes, too, it happens that I fall asleep over my thoughts.

Thus our charming romance, as my delicious mother had called it at the start, came to an end: and it's more than probable that we shall never see each other again. I wrote to her two or three times more, at intervals of a month, to ask her for news and beseech her to forget our misunder-standings: 'Won't you forgive your child? . . .' She has not answered yet.

Was it perhaps my fault after all? I listened too readily to my over-sensitive heart, to my over-lively emotions and to the feasting of my eyes! Of course, she is a most exceptional mother; everyone who knows her says so, it seems, and it may well be that the reader now thinks so too. But do you really imagine I could love her secretly and from a distance, merely as a son of whom one does not speak, a sin of one's youth, the blunder of a too-lively night! . . . I ought not to have told her so often that I adored her, repeating the same thing over and over again, like the poets Lemerre publishes.

Besides, it was too good to last. We had found each other again, I had been able to kiss her, hear her voice, while she called me her child, her darling; and I hoped to see her again. Oh, what a topsy-turvy life! It's generally with one's mother one begins—those charming breasts which one cannot do without—then one grows up, becomes a man, and other loves tend to make one neglect the first a little. But with me it was otherwise. I had found her again after the follies, the peccadilloes, the half-unconscious impulses. What profound pleasures were before us! . . . And she had also deployed all her talent. She wrote me delightful letters, sent me flowers, gave me her photograph, despatched me boxes of sweets. She went to sleep every night reading my books, so she said. My books! She was exaggerating a little. She dreamed also of seeing me again, of becoming my closest and most intimate friend, the friend to whom one tells everything. . . . Oh, had I been able to weep of my distresses to her, when I was a child of twelve or fourteen! She would have comforted me. Poor darling! Oh, yes, poor darling! . . . No, it could not last. My mother was bound to regain her self-control and become once again a respectable lady of principle, after having been my real mama, laughing, intimate, making no fuss and allowing herself to be loved. Oh, marriage! I should have no more nice letters, no more flowers, no more chocolates, no more cakes, etc. And, already, both my greed and my tenderness are aware of a sense of deprivation; I should be hard put to it to say which suffers the most. Madame is far away, cold and dignified, playing at being the mother of a family for good and all and sulking like a coquette to whom one has refused to yield. Silly idiot that she is! Since I never hear from her, I shall no longer dare write. The years will go by, we shall grow older apart, never speaking to each other any more and, one day, one of us will hear that the other is dead. Will he even hear of it? Already my mother's photographs on my mantelpiece and desk, are becoming covered with a fine light dust which makes them less clear-cut, more distant every day. It must be an omen, that's sure, for things are well dusted in my house. The dust of the years will fall on us little by little too, turning our hair grey, then white, dulling our eyes, penetrating our hearts, until the final caper, and that will take place sooner for that dear capricious woman than for me. Adored face, which will turn to me never again. . . . Oh, is it really true that sorrow enables one to write not too badly sometimes?

It is probably best that things should be as they are. Had we met again, might it not have turned out badly? And, when I say badly. . . . How often have I imagined her alone with me, in the same abandon as on that celebrated morning in the Passage Laferrière! Even recently, on the night of the 21st-22nd August, I dreamed of her; we were dining together in a place I did not know and I kissed her bare arms. Had she come to see me, she would certainly have stayed with me, or I would have been continuously at her lodgings. Who knows how far my ardour would have led me? I might have tried to ravish her honour, as they say? Oh, well! . . . Yes, it's really much better as it is.

We were two great amateurs of irony, sensibility and disinterestedness. We wrote extravagant, tender letters to each other, without perhaps believing in them over much, merely, in the end, to make a pirouette with an even wider smile. And even that's not too bad as things go!

What annoys me is the thought that I shall one day suffer for all this. Other people would be unhappy now and recover gradually under the influence of time which, in general, effaces all. But, with me, it's quite the opposite, I know. Even though I am still close to it, all the details of this little history are of quite minor importance to me. But time marches on, and these little details will ripen inside me, and the meeting, the correspondence and the rupture will acquire little by little the same vivid emotional place in my mind as have my childhood memories and the image of my poor Perruche. The day will come when I shall weep about it all alone in my little corner, probably the same day on which I publish our letters; and my dear mama will be dead and I shall have learned to write entertainingly. Anyway, let's laugh till then!

However, that's life. One acts little plays, sometimes sentimental, sometimes ironical, for two or more characters, and it must be admitted the curtain often falls at the moment one least expects it. Anyway, one's lucky they're not tragedies, that no one dies in them, and that's at least one absurdity the less. Then one goes back-stage to hide one's foolish air and to make one's face up again, if—oh, quite by chance!—one happens to have wept. How much better it would be never to have come away, to have remained there smiling gently at the pathetic gestures and tirades of the big parts! But life's as it is. . . . And, one's face made up again as well as one can, one begins once more, in spite of oneself. . . .

When shall I have finished with my metaphors?

In the meantime, I try to make the best of this story and, little though it is, it's better than nothing. I have had the good fortune to see my mother again, and the memory of her face is now more vivid to me, as is the tone of her voice and her way of pronouncing certain words, such as *mama* or *Fanny*, with the accent on the first *a*; as well as the memory of her far from ordinary appearance. To such an extent is this true that, when I meet a woman in the street who resembles her, I am slightly troubled and am apt to start watching her and following her at the risk of seeming what

I am not, as happened indeed only a few weeks ago, in front of the Gymnase, with a young woman who had a somewhat frivolous appearance. We were going in the same direction, and I walked beside her as long as I could, constantly gazing at her with pleasure, taking her in detail by detail and analysing the resemblance. She must certainly have thought I had intentions; from time to time she looked at me encouragingly, slowing her pace a little. . . . If only I had not been in such a hurry! I also acquired Chapters 6 and 7 —what on earth would I have written about without it!—for this book she advised me to write and will never read, for what would be the use of sending it to her? And besides: 'Whatever it contains. . . . Whatever you want to say. . . .' She will have no reason to complain, I think? I also have the packet of letters—hers and copies of mine, a book for later on!—in which I have somewhat made up for all my failures with her. Also five or six dried nosegays at the back of a drawer, some luggage labels, the photographs of her children, and that's about all, yes,—for, as to sorrow, it's not worth talking about. Oh, it's very little, of course! But can you show me many children who have as much? Besides, I don't regret my journey for an instant! . . .

. . . Nevertheless, play me a little tune to make me forget!

Chapter 8

The end of a book is often much inferior to the rest.

STENDHAL

Only a few pages more and I shall have done. I shall resume my evenings with my women friends, as before I began to write this book, and prepare myself gently to write something else, probably a sequel to these reminiscences, if they have gone well and my pockets are full of newspaper cuttings. As you may well imagine, I'm not altogether sorry. And yet, I am not altogether happy at the idea of leaving so soon these pages in which I have recounted, perhaps a little too seriously, so many memories that are dear to me and evoked so many charming images, from the little boy I was to my bolter of a mother, taking in the little friends of my childhood and the grown-up friends of today in passing. What will happen to all these things once they are in the reader's hands? Will he be able to love them as I would like them to be loved, on the right plane, with both emotion and amusement? And have I told them as I should? It seems to me, now that I'm coming to the end of the book, that I could write it better, and, if I obeyed my instincts, I'd begin it all over again.

But I should do no better, or no less badly, that's certain, and the book will have to stay as it is. Besides, I've already spent too long in writing it and the publisher has had to wait for long enough. How many writers in my place, more indifferent to form even than I am, would have finished long ago. Happy authors, who make books as they add up sums.

The only thing is, I wonder what pleasure they derive from it. In my case, it's precisely because I've been concerned with my own pleasure above all else that I have taken rather long to write this book. In telling of these things—oh, true as they are and so much a part of me!—each one of them has stopped me on the way, and I have sat transfixed, pen in hand, as it might be for a photographer, to dream of them at length. From time to time, I have spent a whole evening thus, dreaming about one or two of my memories, or contemplating some face I remembered with a smile. 'As soon as it is written,' I thought, 'it will be done with. But as long as it's inside me, it's part of life. Soon, it will scarcely belong to me any more. Let me therefore enjoy it just once again.' And what an apotheosis! Now that I read it over again, I find barely twenty pages in the whole book that satisfy me. It must, however, be like most books, made up of passages to like or dislike and others that are unbearably boring.

Besides, despite the promise I made myself to work hard till it was finished, I have often left the manuscript to go and see my friends and take a cure with them in one or other of those places, amid music, lights and people. They would have had their doubts about me if I had remained too long without going to see them, and I would have run a risk of being replaced. Besides, life goes on; work becomes tedious after a while; and it is a sound plan to assure oneself a happy middle-age and quiet last years with the women. Besides, those few evenings, two or three a week, were not lost time as far as my writing was concerned. Many of my friends might write less boring books if they knew how to provide their genius with a little relaxation of this kind from time to time. While I was enjoying myself intellectually with these women, my work continued to develop in my mind, almost in spite of myself. No one suspected it, not even they, who were moreover busy enough about other matters, nor the comrades I met here and there, so much did I look as if I were amusing myself. Nevertheless, some of the most sensational phrases in this book came to me in cafés or on promenades, while idling, chatting and watching, though sometimes scarcely seeing, the pathetic, weary faces of women. But, who can tell? This book might have been really good if I had written it with such phrases alone, and I may well have wasted too little time 'waiting for the moment of genius,' as Stendhal said. Nevertheless, he once expressed regret at having spent so much time waiting for it. But who would not be willing to suffer a regret of this kind and to have written such books! One writes well and has ideas only at moments of pleasure and emotion. To try to write when neither moved nor happy is often to waste one's time and produce nothing of value. I hope I'm being interesting at the moment!

If only, what's more, I hadn't faltered, except at moments, in my resolution to pose as a best-selling novelist! But, since I finished Chapter 7, at least a fortnight has elapsed. I have spent it entirely in the Rue Laferrière, with a new friend whom I met only recently, while idling as I said above, and through the intermediary of my other women friends. I had asked them for ages to find me something in that street! I was so moved after that chapter, that I wanted to allow a little time to elapse before starting on this one. Without that, I might have gone astray among my tears and failed to finish this book on a properly sensible note. I therefore took the parcel of manuscript and, taking advantage of my new friend's periodical indisposition—I'll write of her at greater length one day—I went and took up my quarters with her to correct it, add a general idea here and there, and enjoy once more the pleasures I had recorded. An easy, idle labour, which one can do without too much concentration, rather as a woman, having brightened her eyes with a little black and her lips with a little rouge, powders her face before going out. Besides, is not writing merely putting one's own gloss on the words everyone uses?

I have often thought, during this restorative fortnight, of what Lucian says in his *De Domo*. It is indeed true that certain surroundings dispose one to work more than others! Of course, I am not speaking of that vulgar work which consists in taking a pen, ink and paper and writing what one wants to write. For that sort of work any surroundings are suitable, even those apalling studies of fashionable authors, encumbered like antique shops, which we see in the photographs of our contemporaries at home. I am speaking of the sort of work, the only true work, which consists in doing nothing, in thinking merely of what one wants to do, of absorbing it, seeing it in oneself, either in fragments or as a whole, etc., etc. The correcting of my chapters somewhat resembled this process. Sitting on my new friend's *chaise-longue*, I worked with application, stopping every five minutes to rest, caressing with my eyes the youthful, frivolous décor about me, from the little white-painted table on which I wrote, to the poster of the Folies-Bergère, Cléo de Mérode dancing, attached to the wall with pins. Two paces from me was the mantelpiece with photographs, a travelling clock, used envelopes, a knitting needle and ribbons lying about, with, on the other side of me, the low, perpetually ready bed on which I placed my pages as I finished them. In a little neighbouring room, through the open door, I could see the dressing-table, with its flagons, pots and brushes, a thousand accessories of coquetry and the profession, then, a little further away, the mirror, in which I could see myself from where I sat, looking important and lazy in front of my papers. My friend was fussing round, doing nothing except make a lot of noise, continuously moving about, and every now and then making an intelligent remark such as: 'Shall we go out tonight? . . .' Or: 'Really, do you mean to say you wrote all that? . . .' while humming in the most charming manner in the world the *Polka des Anglais*, which might really have been composed for the occasion.

As you can see, this professional interior of another kind was far different from the famous studies, so intensely academic, with their innumerable books, vast tables, adjustable stools and high desks. But I've ceased to think books look nice against walls. I prefer a light paper, with two or three drawings in narrow frames, and this woman's room pleased me, as I wrote on a little light table, in the company of this half-naked creature, and without a single book in my vicinity. On this very *chaise-longue* on which I was sitting, my new friend, on ordinary days, must certainly make love and put on a bit of an act with a variety of gentlemen, without attaching any more importance to it than they do. A little satisfaction, a little money and each goes away happy, no longer even thinking of the act in which he has just indulged. Outside was the street, the most delicious of all streets, with its houses of assignation, from whose windows, with their half-closed shutters, came lively little whispers full of promise for the passer-by. All this gave me talent and I wished I had not written my book, so that I could write it here, beside this loose young woman, reclining in her dressing-gown, only a few yards from that house where, on a morning in 1881, I went so ingenuously to visit my pretty mother, and right in the centre of my childhood's district which has still changed so little. . . . No! I really must not begin all over again!

In any case, whether I had started this book again or written it there, I would have paid no more attention to the style. I don't care if it's ill-written, and I had other things to do, when writing it, than waste my time polishing my phrases. Besides, literary preciosity and starting afresh over and over again—the same page fifteen times only two years ago—are over and done with as far as I'm concerned. The great mechanical stylists, with the boring regularity of their phrases, have disgusted me with style for ever. Poor books, so harmonious if you like, but so boring! There is no rhetoric in the books I like, indeed there are even imperfections, but the man who wrote them is worth all the Flauberts in the world. Oh, the beauty, the absorbing interest, often, of an ill-turned phrase that has nevertheless been left in its pristine truth and not distorted by art! But there! You must know how to read, and have read a lot, and compared and weighed the duplicity of that word 'art', which fools delight in. Then one discards many admirations, and these so-called great books don't stand up for a minute.

I can say this, and you can think I'm posing if you like, but nowadays, when I sit down to write, my difficulty is to find the first phrase; afterwards, however, I no longer pay attention to my phrases, I write just with my idea before me and as it comes. If a phrase does not please me, I don't rearrange it, I make another, that's all. If by chance there are a few phrases in this book that are not bad, it's no thanks to me, it's merely that they came that way and I am not even sure I don't prefer the others, with all their faults, because they sometimes express an emotion better, the very nuance of a memory. The further I go, the more I think that one should perhaps not start writing till the age of forty. Before that, one is not mature, but too ardent, too sensitive, so to speak, and also inclined to like literature too much, which falsifies everything. I should have liked to write this book in the form of *Letters* or *Memoirs*, the only kinds of writing that count, with short precise phrases, pointed and curt, like the descriptions in a catalogue or pretty much so. I am some distance from that, I know. Perhaps my mother's encouragement helped to lead me into the wrong path? Such absurd tenderness, so useless! Admirable irony too though.... Well, it will have to be for another time! Besides, perhaps one day I'll write this book again, in some fifty pages; I am so well aware of what ought to be cut out. And yet.... But I'm not satisfied with this book, of course, or at least, if it pleases me on one day, it displeases me on the three days following. It is none the less true that I have felt the things I have recorded exactly as I have written them. My nature is here in conflict with my taste, that's all. It's very amusing.

All the same, I'm beginning to think, and better late than never, that it's time I ended this chapter, which is in any case quite useless, despite all the intelligent things I've said in it. I should nevertheless like to have said a few words about the truth of this book, in which I have given names and dates wherever possible, indeed to such an extent that many people I have mentioned, particularly in the chapter about my childhood, may well disapprove. Of course, as far as my women friends are concerned, I have omitted minor details; I have not given their names and addresses. For if I had, crowds of people would no doubt have rushed to them and they exhaust themselves quite enough already without that. Besides this book is not after all, indeed is very far from being, a *Directory of Paris Prostitutes*! I should also have liked to poke a little fun at the reproaches that will doubtless be hurled at me for having spoken in this book of that astonishing creature who brought me into the world and for having made use of my joy at seeing her again so soon, and also of our correspondence. But I had better make an end. I have preached enough in my other chapters to exempt me from doing it again in this one. Besides, the literary critics will have it in for me if I continue to take the wind out of their sails by saying everything there is to say about this book. I don't want to annoy those gentlemen whose articles are so useful.

PART II
In Memoriam

Time does not console, it effaces.

GUIZOT

PART II : IN MEMORIAM

Once again, I have seen death close at hand. When the number of our dead increases, it is a sign we are growing older. My old nurse Marie died in 1887 or 1888; my aunt Fanny getting on for two years ago; and now my father! And one day, sooner or later, it will be the turn of that delicious creature who gave me birth. In the meantime, a friend goes here and there. . . . I'm becoming more and more of a lonely man, sitting by his fireside or in music-halls, cigar in hand and full of reveries. What peace!

Today, I want to put it to good use by writing a little of my father and his death. It will be an opportunity of diverting myself for fifteen or twenty evenings, including my hours of idling, and to write a few more pages of childhood reminiscence. These memories are so alive, it needs but little to make me surrender myself to them utterly. A child jumping on to a woman's lap in the doorway of a house on a summer's evening, a little boy with curious eyes walking alone with a man, even the aspect of certain districts of Paris, according to the time of year, and I am suddenly transported back twenty-five years and I see myself, indeed I actually feel myself, jumping on to my old nurse's lap once more or walking with short steps, hand in hand with my father, or, again, wandering for hours together through the Saint-Georges and Rochechouart districts in which I grew up. And it is even truer today when I turn to the subject of these pages. The exigencies of literature are the only cloud in my sky; and they are so important, don't you think? One can make every possible preparation for writing and discipline one's mind. Yet, when one least expects it, one memory leads to another, which leads to a third, and you are in the grip of emotion. Just think of it, so many past years! So you see, my transitions will probably not be very brilliantly managed.

When was this father among fathers born? I don't know. Two dates were put on his tombstone. I can never remember the first one. It appears he was sixty-nine. I calculate: 1903 less sixty-nine, which makes 1834. Let's say 1834.

I know nothing of his origins, nor of his youth. He came to Paris at the age of twenty, and went to work with his uncle, a jeweller, whose shop, called À la Maison Rouge, was in the Faubourg Montmartre, quite close to Notre-Dame-de-Lorette, a few yards from the draper's shop with the sign François les Bas bleus. The shop still exists and, when I was a child, we had at home a fine painted wooden clock, decorated with gilt bronzes, and bearing our name on the face.

It is probable that the jeweller's shop did not much attract him. Indeed, I read in the newspapers, when he retired from the Comédie-Française, that he had been trained at the Conservatoire, in Régnier's class. He left with a second prize for comedy in 1858 I believe, and with a *proxime accessit* for tragedy, played at the Odéon, at the little theatre in the Rue de la Tour-d'Auvergne, at the Porte-Saint-Martin, at the Matinées Ballande, of which he was manager, and elsewhere too. It even seems that he very nearly played at the Comédie one night as Thiron's

understudy. But what does that matter? I knew him only
as prompter at the Comédie, where his friend Maubant had
got him the job in about 1874 or 1875. He carried on this
duty till April 1897. This was how, from the moment I
could walk, I so often wandered about the backstage
corridors of this theatre, a curious, shy little boy whom
the ladies made much of because of his beautiful eyes.
Those years passed too quickly! I grew up little by little
and became a young man, till one day these same ladies
showed greater reserve. How illogical women are!

It seems he was irresistible, that all the women fell in
love with him, and that he had that good fortune which
counts in a man's life. I remember a dinner, some fifteen
years ago, at which actors were present and someone saying
that in his day he had had all the prettiest women in Paris.
Why should one be surprised? A woman who knew him
very well told me, soon after his death, that in his prime,
which lasted a long time, he often went to bed with two
women at once and took them each three or four times, in
his stride, as it were. There must be a certain sentiment in
love, of course, but not too much.

I know nothing of his first mistresses, but I knew
some of the others, from my Aunt Fanny and my mother,
the two sisters, to the last, my present stepmother, whom
he decided eventually to marry, after living with her for
fifteen years. My mother told me about it in October 1901
during those three wonderful days I spent with her in
Calais, where we had gone, she and I, to be present at
Fanny's death-bed, and met unexpectedly after more than
twenty years' separation. He had first known Fanny, the
elder of the two, by whom he had a daughter called Hélène.
He already had a great reputation as a libertine, and his

daughter was immediately sent to her grandmother's in the Rue d'Odessa, where she was to die in 1880. For all that he swore and threatened, and I can imagine the violence with which he did it, for he was hasty and fiery by temperament, he could obtain no other concession than permission to go and see her from time to time. Fanny used to say that if the child had been left in his care he would undoubtedly have ended by going to bed with her. Yet, the poor child had but little in the way of looks! Next it was my mother's turn. One evening, when she was sixteen or seventeen, she was at the house of the two lovers, her sister and my father. It was very late, and they hesitated to let her go home to her parents alone, right at the other end of Montparnasse. My father suggested she should spend the night with them and, since there was only one bed, they all three slept in it together. My mother was still innocent, so it appears, but this did not embarrass my father in the least or prevent his having relations with his mistress beside her. 'At the end of an hour, I knew what a man and a woman could do together,' my mother said when she told me of it. A little while afterwards, my father could think of nothing better than to take her for a mistress too. I am not sure I am right, and that it was not that night their liaison began. My mother's words seemed to hint at it and, furthermore, my father was not the man to hesitate for long when an innocent young girl was in question. All this naturally scandalised poor Fanny, who found herself left in the lurch, and also my future grandmother, who was a particularly strict and prudish bourgeoise. A sound woman, my grandmother! I had the pleasure of making her acquaintance at Calais at the time I met my mother again, and she did not conceal from me that she had never forgiven my father for having seduced both her daughters. All mothers are like that. It is never their child who began it, it is always the *other* who has *seduced*. The sacred principles of the family and the domestic virtues must be safeguarded! Mlle Jeanne, for that was my mother's Christian name, was shown the door, as they say in novelettes, and set up with my father. They had, I believe, a first child who did not live. Then I was born, with for father a man who was always chasing new women, and for mother a young woman with an adorable face. He was then thirty-eight. She was twenty. It was the 18th January 1872, at about one o'clock in the morning at No. 37, Rue Molière, close to the Palais-Royal. My sister Hélène, who was also my cousin, since she was the daughter of my mother's sister, must then have been six or seven. A little later, on the 11th March, I was baptised at the church of Saint-Roch, with for godmother Mlle Blanche Boissard, soon to be Mlle Bianca of the Comédie-Française, and who was one day to be godmother to Mme Réjane's children. My mother is Parisian, the daughter and granddaughter of Parisians. She has told me, but too shortly, of her early youth in the Rue Monsieur-le-Prince, where her parents then lived. A precocious child, I've no doubt. She is so delightfully different from most mothers, who are so tiresomely prejudiced about what constitutes good behaviour. When I was a child I certainly derived from her a notion of what a 'cocotte' might be, as I then called it. And it was thus I found her again at Calais, still very slim and dark, and with the same free and easy ways. She had completely set aside her pose of being a married woman and the mother of a family, to become simply a charming woman in my arms. That dear face was only a little touched by the years. . . . Three days, a mere three days! Let us think of it no more. I have inherited much from her in facial expression, and as far as character goes changeability and prodigality, a capacity to yield only to regret it afterwards, and never to be satisfied with anything. However little that may be, it's still something. The pity of it is, and this goes for the reader too, that I know no more about her than I do of my father, even though I have made a little progress in this direction since meeting her again. Let's see what it all adds up to. She was on the stage till about 1890; began a serious liaison in Geneva and married a few years later; had two children, a boy and a girl; and that's about all I know of her. Oh, one more detail! She was admirable as a male impersonator, so it appears. What promise was latent in that single fact!

Since my father and mother were both on the stage and playing in different places, I was put out to nurse. I was first with a woman who very nearly let me die of neglect, then with another, who was as good as she could be, on the extreme edge of Paris, in the Chaussée du Maine. I still have a few little photographs of that time, in which I am to be seen in my nurse's arms, looking very wide-awake and with a little whip in my hand. These will certainly be the earliest photographs the public will have of me, when I am famous and the newspapers publish my pictures. When I was about two and a half, I was returned to my father's house. I do not know precisely where my mother then was, in Bordeaux I think. My father and she must have separated some time before. I have never discovered any details about that, nor which of them was at fault, if fault there was; for, indeed, one may separate simply to have a change or, again, my mother may merely have left to fulfil an engagement, the separation taking place later and quite naturally. My mother has indeed told me that my father was avaricious, brutal and licentious, but she was pretty flighty too, it appears. The things I've heard about her! ... Oh, I am not setting myself up to judge her, nor does it embarrass me at all. I shall say, as the song does 'That's how I love her,' and it seems to me that, were she different, she would not be my mother.

My father was then living at 13, Rue des Martyrs. I found there an old nurse, my dear Marie Pezé, whom he must have engaged for me. How patiently devoted to me that woman was for nearly ten years, often having to take my side against my father; she put up with a great deal rather than abandon me. He had his theatre, his café, his friends, his dogs and, above all, his women. Oh, those women! His life at that time was filled with them. Every morning, he came down from his room with a new one, to Marie's great scandal, and she did her best to prevent my noticing anything. I can still remember one of those creatures, she was dark and opulent and had insolent eyes and, a little later, when we were living at 21, Rue des Martyrs, she came on several consecutive days. My father had been running after her for some time, and I knew her a little because I had on occasion been present at their preliminary conversations. At that time, 13, Rue des Martyrs and 14, Rue Notre-Dame-de-Lorette, where there was a café, communicated, and that was where they met on a little flight of steps at the further end of the second court-yard of No. 13, when my father crossed the courtyards of the two houses to reach the café more quickly. What has become of that pretty girl who always wanted me to call her 'Mama', when she met me in the morning as she came down from my father's room? I think of her each time I go for a walk in the Rue des Martyrs and indeed, latterly, thought I recognised her, which resulted in my making a fool of myself. I had followed a woman as far as No. 3, Rue Clauzel, thinking to question her, but she looked me haughtily up and down and summoned her concierge. At that time she must have been about twenty-five, and now therefore nearly fifty. I would like to meet her again, I think, and talk to her about her old lover.

As for my mother, I still barely knew her. I do not know where she was acting and making love. My old nurse, who wrote to her from time to time, spoke of her occasionally but without its affecting me very much. As far as I was concerned, my nurse was my mother, and I called her mama too. The very idea of the other one, 'the real one', as she said, painfully aroused my shyness. The first time I saw her at this period was in 1876. She told me this herself during the remarkable five months' correspondence that followed our meeting at Calais, and in which she was kind enough to give me her own memories of the period in a long letter. We were still living in the same flat, at 13, Rue des Martyrs, that she had also apparently lived in, and we went, both of us together with Marie, to the Comédie. But try as I will, all I have been able to recollect of this visit is a tiny fragment of the play then running at the Comédie, *Le Supplice d'une Femme*, of which I very well remember one scene with an actress called Mlle Croizette, I think, sitting on a sofa on the right of the stage with a child beside her. I remember another occasion, in 1877, rather better; it was a few years before the fabulous interview in the Passage Laferrière, which I recounted in *Le Petit Ami*. It was at Marie's, in her poor little room in the

Rue Clauzel. My mother was passing through Paris on her way to Berlin and had come to see me with my grandmother. I was rather ill and lay with my face to the wall. I could not have been more gracious. My grandmother came up to me first. 'Say "how do you do" to the lady!' said Marie. When I had been told to do this several times, I consented at last to show my face and say 'how do you do' more or less politely, only to turn my head away again at once. 'What, aren't you going to say anything to the other lady?' Marie said, indicating my mother who was approaching in her turn. 'How many more of them are there?' I cried. I was a charming child and, indeed am still rather like that today, with my face turned towards my reveries. And there was not to be any more of mama in the future than there had been in the past. She left that day after about five minutes, and I had to wait four years in the first instance before seeing her again, then twenty years, and now—oh, now, it's probably all over and done with. Her tenderness and Geneva are both so far away! All the railways in the world could not suffice.

Then the day came when my father decided to get rid of Marie in order to have greater freedom in his new love-affair with the young woman who was one day to become my stepmother. It was at the end of 1880 or the beginning of 1881. He was then forty-eight, and she was fifteen and a half or sixteen. She lived in the district and walked down the Rue des Martyrs every morning. I can see her still, slight, her hair in a curly fringe, trotting along with a saucy air. My father met her several days running when going in the morning to his café at the corner of the Rue des Martyrs and the Rue Hippolyte-Lebas. As he did to all the women he liked the look of, he put his dog-whip round her neck.

He was still a very handsome man, tall, fresh-complexioned, broad-shouldered, and his hair was still black. They soon got to know each other and she came to sleep with him several nights running. My old nurse remonstrated with him more strongly than ever about such a liaison, put me forward as an argument, talked of the deplorable example he was setting me, etc. etc. He lost his temper, she refused to give way, and he sacked her. What a marvellous gift of memory and emotion I have! I can see the setting, the dining-room of the damp little maisonette in which we lived at that time. I can hear the voices of my father and of Marie, I can recall their physical appearance, and see myself, sitting in a corner, attentive and appalled, and the memory, as are all my memories, is so vividly present to my mind that I need but to cease writing for a moment to see the whole scene again as if it had happened only yesterday. And the very least I needed to do was to pay attention to it, moreover. Till then, I had been happy, happy with a sort of innate happiness I have never been able to recover, and probably never shall recover. My old nurse spoilt me and was unable to refuse to satisfy any of my caprices. She carried me in the street, sang by my bed at night to make me go to sleep. I can still hear her low, quavering voice. I can still hear the songs she sang. Indeed, I often sing them softly to myself, like a great child! Sometimes it was a passage from the *Noces de Jeannette*:

> En le choisissan-ant } bis
> J'avais cru bien fai-re
> Ma pauvre âme est pleine
>   D'un mortel souci
> C'était bien la peine, etc., etc.

Sometimes it was another song, of which the chorus ran:

> En attendant, sur mes genoux,
> Beau général, endormez-vous. . . .

But now all that was over. I was going to have to begin to learn about life, real life. I should have to walk alone, stand upright too, if not. . . . How often did that dear old woman spend her own money on clothing me, for my father did not always think of it, or on taking me to the Fernando Circus or to Robert-Houdin, or on buying me presents to amuse me and relieve me, indeed, of that continuous melancholy I displayed. It got on my father's nerves; he said he couldn't understand it and shook me. . . . But she was tenderness itself! As I was saying, I've got a wonderful gift of emotion!

At this actual moment, I should like to be a few pages older. With what I wrote in *Le Petit Ami*, I have practically exhausted the memories of the happy times of my childhood. Such enchanting days, filled with gracious, loving characters, against that peculiarly Parisian background! Now I must pass on to those of the years I lived with my father and his new mistress after the departure of my old nurse. In spite of all my talent, how am I going to manage it? I should like the reader, who may perhaps be rejoicing at the change, to see me at the moment of writing this paragraph, doing my best, though without undue excess, to prepare myself for it. The fact is that these memories in my second manner are somewhat diverse. I hardly know how to set about them, and there will be quite a number I shall put aside. They are such an old story, and so many books have already told it. Characters: a helpless child and a woman who is not his mother. Except for a few details, the reader would not lose much and I would also have preferred never to know it. In any case, I want to give myself the luxury of pretending to forget it here. Pride? A sort of dignity? Yes, perhaps, if you insist. But, above all, I would be inspiring only sympathy! Thanks for the opportunity!

Before beginning, I should like to describe the frame in which I began first to realise that everything is not always rosy in life. In the courtyard of 21, Rue des Martyrs, on the left, was a maisonette consisting of a ground and first floor. On the ground floor, beyond a little court, was the kitchen, the dining-room and the drawing-room and, on the first floor, a bedroom (my father's) and a dressing-room. In the middle of the little twisting staircase that led up to the first floor was a little door. That was my room, my *first room*, a narrow little room with a very low ceiling, lit by an absurdly small window, which gave on to the courtyard. On the ground floor opposite, which gave on to a garden behind a railing with in front of it a fountain with a large basin, lived at that time M. Lesueur, a proof-reader on the *Figaro*, which publication he so disarmingly threw in one of the director's faces, having first made all his family defecate in it. All this still exists. The curious can go and see it for themselves. Perhaps one day a plaque will be put up! Whenever I pass by, I go in as far as the end of the entrance-arch. Our maisonette usually has its shutters closed. M. Lesueur's ground-floor is now occupied by a carpet and furniture shop. I stay there a few minutes gazing at it all with a feeling of lively egotism. And each time the concierge looks at me with surprise and suspicion, not knowing whether he ought to stop me and question me. He can probably never make up his mind, for he has not spoken to me yet. I would tell him what it's all about if I had to. But then I should have to talk to him every time, ask him how he is etc., the usual concierge gossip! And all my pleasure would be spoiled.

At that time, our concierge was called Rivière, 'the *père* Rivère', he was a widower, and a tailor into the bargain, and ran after all the maids in the house. An excellent man. I can still see him, always in waistcoat and shirt-sleeves, with a kind face under rumpled hair, Austrian moustaches and whiskers, spectacles balanced on a red nose, and a cap always rather askew. One day, my father hit him because he made remarks about his behaviour, the number of women he brought home, etc. The author of my being didn't joke about these matters. On each side of the entrance was a shop. The one on the left was a little shop selling tea and coffee, as it does today, and was then owned by a couple called Guichardot, the woman with an ailing little face, the man a tall, red-headed fellow with long whiskers. The shop on the right sold linen, haberdashery and hosiery. It was kept by a Mme Nadeau, who had two charming daughters, Jeanne and Marguerite, with whom I often played all day in the courtyard of the house. Some ten years ago, as I was going along the Rue de Sèvres, I recognised a face I had seen somewhere before in one of those hawkers of haberdashery who used to stand with their baskets along the wall of the Laënnec Hospital. I searched my memory for a moment. It was Mme Nadeau. I spoke to her and told her who I was. She told me she lived in the Rue Saint-Romain, at No.—, with her two daughters, grown-up girls now! I was to go and see them, but for no particular reason did nothing about it. Jeanne and Marguerite! Alas, they will have grown older as I have. Recently, I have often searched the district of the Rue de Sèvres to try to find them, asking the concierges, the shop-keepers, going endlessly to and fro. But a lot of the Rue Saint-Romain has been pulled down, and people listen to me with odd looks, rather as if I were a creditor in search of a debtor, and I have got nowhere as yet.

Now for those happy years I told you about, or at least for as much of them as I wish to recount. When I come to think of it, I feel a sort of contemptuous pity for those two people: my father and his mistress. He, at least, remained what he had always been, brutal, casual and a libertine. But, as for her! Our relations became established from the very first day. Did she not take it upon herself to prevent my going out for a walk before dinner as I was accustomed to do? Explain things to her as I would, she refused to understand and, in face of her stubbornness, I had to resort to throwing a full ink-pot at her head. Of course, it was I who was in the wrong. When my father came home, she told him. I had assaulted his new darling! Results followed quickly. He broke a toy my mother had given me on her last visit into smithereens before my eyes. But the best was a little later, when we had gone to Courbevoie, where she felt herself to be really mistress of the house. Then she began to take her role seriously and stuck at nothing, ill-treatment, deprivations, underhand tricks, etc. In particular, she appeared deeply concerned about my education, and in this respect left my old nurse Marie far behind. How can I give the reader some idea of it without shocking him too much? When she felt in the mood, she would tell me how my mother—and what charming names she called her!—allowed herself to be had in cabs, or she would explain, when she made me help her make her bed in the

mornings, precisely what caresses she lavished on my
father, emphasising her confidences with a peculiarly
expressive oral mime! I ask you, taking one thing with
another, whether these things were particularly odd? I do
not know what the reader thinks, but I certainly discovered,
later on, that they were not. It is certainly true that I was
not very encouraging! Oh, my future stepmother might
well exhaust herself on the subject! I was so dull-witted in
these matters that I listened without understanding, and
all her symbolism was in vain! And in spite of having a
father such as mine, of having seen so many women come
down from his room in the morning, and of having so many
little girls as playmates! This shows the influence of
environment! I can assert that, even two or three years
later, I still knew nothing, even in imagination, of the
physical gestures of love. For all that more knowing contemporaries talked about them in my presence, what they
described seemed so odd to me that I refused to believe it.
Happily, my future stepmother had a vocation, and
nothing could stop her. I remember certain afternoons,
when she made me take my trousers off, to mend them so
she said, and then immediately came to tease me in the
corner where I sat waiting ingenuously, my legs under a
rug; or when she came and plagued me at night, when I
was in bed, staying an hour or more and pulling the bed-
clothes off, do what I would to get rid of her. I remember
one night in her room at our Courbevoie house. It was
winter. I was then fourteen or fifteen. We were both sitting
by the fire, doing and saying nothing. I can see us now:
she was sitting on the window side, and I was in the
opposite corner, with my chair against a backgammon
table that stood there then. My trousers happened to be

unbuttoned, though I was not aware of it. She drew my attention to the fact, at first reproachfully, and then. . . . 'But what an enchanting stepmother!' the immoral will say. But I had morals, I still have, and all these amiabilities had no effect on me.

From about this period there are two or three other memories I particularly wish to make use of. Not content with preventing my going out, my future stepmother often shut me up alone in the house. There was, of course, the garden, which was large enough to play in, but I had already fallen in love with Paris from the bottom of my heart and had no use for nature. So I would spend the whole day in the dining-room, lying on the carpet under the table, my head among the legs or on the chest of one of the dogs, which was called Tabac, like another we had at an earlier date, at the time of my old nurse, when we lived in Paris. It was my best companion and I, who have always been so sensitive to gentle, liquid eyes, whether they be those of a human being or of an animal, took the opportunity of dreaming at my ease. In this way, I spent many days thinking of myself, of my childish miseries, talking to myself in a low voice, telling myself I was alone in the world, with no one to love or amuse me, poor darling! And what I'm going to say is not an author's embellishment: I often imagined the day of my father's death, what it would be like, what would happen etc. And real tears came to my eyes, while I pressed myself still closer to the dog. Oh, I must stop, I'm becoming sentimental, I feel it, and I've still got so many pages to write! Sometimes, too, by means of the key of a chest-of-drawers that fitted, I searched my father's cupboard. There were obscene pictures which interested me vaguely because of the extravagant postures they illustrated. I could also look at his photograph album, full of photographs of women, all with very intimate dedications. There was quite a number of my mother and that was another great subject of reverie for me. One day, making a more detailed search than usual, I found some old letters from my mother. They dated from the time they were still together. My mother was in Bordeaux and she wrote telling him to be good and not to pay too many attentions to certain women in the Passage du Saumon. After eighteen years, I can still remember a sentence from one of these letters: 'I know so well how you cajole women,' my mother wrote, 'and with what pleasure you let yourself go, as soon as one of them seems to be making advances to you.' What a curious phenomenon memory is! The older one gets, the further back it goes. At the time, these letters reminded me of nothing, and it was only much later that, when thinking of them, I remembered having indeed gone with my father one day to visit a lady who lived in the Passage du Saumon. It was on the right, as you entered from the Rue Montmartre, and there were a number of young women in the house who all called my father: Léautaud—just that. I even wonder now whether it was not perhaps one of those friendly houses. If it was I can no longer boast of having never set foot in one! The memory of these letters returned to me in Calais, when my mother told me, as if I had asked her, of all the trouble she had had with my father. I had sometimes been astonished at the number of successes with women attributed to him, not knowing anything as yet of his remarkable amorous capacities, and I wanted to find out about them. What a good opportunity it was! My mother seemed at first to look at me in astonishment. She must certainly have thought that men can sometimes be very stupid in these matters when it concerns another man. 'Oh, yes, you know, he was very good-looking!' she ended by saying. 'He had wonderful eyes too, it was enough for him to look at you to. . . .' I can really find only dots to render what my mother appeared to imply by leaving the phrase in the air. If any women read this passage, they will no doubt be able to complete the sentence. You can write to me at the *Mercure*. I shall be glad to receive letters on the subject.

But I must go back to when my old nurse left and continue my panegyric. My future stepmother had barely come to live in the house when she developed a craze for the stage. It was a question of contagion, no doubt. There are, indeed, people who blush to earn their living as servants and yet fill the part very well on the stage. Besides, it is so easy to become an actor or an actress! There is no need to be intelligent, rather the contrary. The stupider one is the better, and the first idiot, the first goose who comes along can succeed in it, with no other talent or preparation than the learning of a certain language and certain tricks. The one thing that really surprises me in the circumstances is my father's patience. Besides, he was very far from being a fool! I can see him, I can hear him still, making his new mistress rehearse in our little drawing-room, at 21, Rue des Martyrs, the part of Henriette in *Femmes Savantes*, while I watched them both from my corner. They do it no better at the Conservatoire, I'm sure! For instance, somewhere in the part of Henriette there is a line which begins: 'Ah!' My father had just uttered this 'Ah!' one evening with the proper intonation, when my future stepmother, discarding her pose, rushed to him in horror and asked him what the matter was. She simply thought he was feeling ill. One must, I know, make allowances for a ladies' man; and for the particular relationship in which my father found himself regarding this young person. New brooms sweep clean, and it even happens that the least gallant will listen to a woman's chatter when they know they are going to make love to her when she has done. But this was really going too far! However, I must record the fact that my father quickly grew tired of it. And soon it was no longer in rehearsing that his free evenings were spent, but in other pleasures, more real, and also more advantageous to him. I had, of course, my part as always. As soon as dinner was over, I was sent up to my room and locked in, left alone in the dark in spite of all my tears and so lively a terror that at night, in my dreams, I still suffered from it. Love, love, when you hold us in your clutches!

I lived this happy life for some time. Then my father decided to go to live in the country, and in 1882 we moved to Courbevoie. A pretty place, if you happen to know it? At that period, it was adorned by a night-soil deposit, whose disappearance has left the inhabitants ill at ease. We were hardly installed in this delightful suburb, when my stepmother's dramatic aspirations became stronger than ever. She began taking French lessons with a local teacher, a man whom I have since known, called Houlé, and I am not surprised that she learned so little, at least of French. Then, her studies completed, her journeys began, sumptuous engagements in celebrated provincial theatres, where she must have shone in the chorus, at least. What a repertory she displayed to us on her return, a splendid collection of such well-known pieces of chamber music as *Mascotte, Grand Mongol, Mousquetaires au Couvent, Cloches de Corneville, Petit Duc, Rip* and others! It was lucky she had studied French and Molière, they must have been useful to her. When, during her holidays, she suddenly burst out into one of these great arias, it was so melodious that even the dog accompanied her. Her first engagement was in the theatre at Calais, a theatre and town where she was to make the acquaintance of my Aunt Fanny, who had been there a considerable time. My father even wrote to Fanny recommending the new 'star' to her, and this excellent woman looked after her as best she could throughout the time they were together. Then other engagements followed, there and elsewhere, sometimes for a month, sometimes for six, with intervals of 'resting', and my future stepmother would warn us of her arrival no earlier than the day before. You may think these caprices must have disorganised the household and embarrassed my father, who found himself left suddenly alone with me? But, indeed, my future stepmother had barely left when another woman came to take her place. Sometimes it was a maid, since my father went to an employment agency at 66, Faubourg Montmartre, where he was known and could always be sure of finding what he wanted. Sometimes it was just merely a woman. The things I saw, of every kind, particularly with the maids! There was one, for instance, who asked immediately on arrival where the barracks were. Another, who was pretty, quite crazy, but had a certain distinction—a maid by misadventure no doubt—was wildly hysterical! When it came over her, as she said, she was quite unable to restrain herself and, dropping everything, rushed off to take the train to Paris to be satisfied by her lover. There was another again, when we were no longer living in the Avenue de la République, but at 12 or 14, Rue de l'Ouest. She was called Clotilde, was fifteen or sixteen years of age, with a little face like the Virgin Mary's, and her mother, moreover, was an old bigot who lived in the district. She had been taken on to help my future step-mother, who had just had her son, and since there was no room for her in the house she was put to sleep with me. It was in 1885 and I was thirteen. My father always had a number of dogs, and at the time I am speaking of a bitch had just had a litter of puppies. The puppies were, as always, enchanting, and Clotilde and I often took one or two of them to bed with us. And, one evening, when we had been in bed for some time and I was already probably half asleep, I happened to put out my hand by chance and felt a little warm, hairy body in the bed. 'Hullo,' I said to Clotilde, as I automatically began stroking it, 'so you've brought one of the puppies to bed with you?' She replied in a very odd way, something that sounded more like a sigh than speech, and, as I continued stroking, I felt that the object of my caresses was lending itself to them very well, indeed facilitating them, even giving me a little more room. Alas, after all I have said, you will not be surprised! Such engaging manners left me cold, I remained in error as to the animal, really believing it to be a puppy, and after a moment or two I turned over and went to sleep. There are a number of such missed opportunities in my life, two or three from ignorance, the rest from shyness. That was the first—of the first. After all, why not admit it about all those maids? I even went once to the celebrated employment agency in the Faubourg Montmartre to fetch one myself. A fine looking girl, I remember, whose company embarrassed me a good deal during the railway journey and who told me dirty stories in the kitchen the very first night. She insisted on giving me the address of her room in Paris, in the Rue de

Tocqueville, but I have forgotten the number, so that I might go and see her on Sundays. I was then sixteen or seventeen, and, it seems, far from ugly, or so I was told a few years later, when I had my first mistress, and I'll write about that one day. So splendid an opportunity rather excited me and I gave way to an act of onanism in her presence, which grieved her. Such ardour, she said (she used a more lively word), might have been put to better use. When she had gone to bed, I plucked up sufficient courage to go to her room. She naturally gave me a very welcoming reception, but I knew less than nothing, while the slightest noise in the house put me off, not to mention a certain physical disaccord which created great difficulties for me. In spite of all the help she gave me, I left the room a few minutes later in the same state I had entered it. After a few days, for some reason I have forgotten, probably a row with my stepmother, this girl left us, and lack of freedom, I expect, as much as my extreme timidity at the idea of such a step, prevented my going to see her at the address she had given me. Many years later, when certain business took me to that district, I could never pass through the Rue de Tocqueville without dreaming a little. It seems I am becoming sentimental!

But I want particularly to talk of one of these changes caused by my future stepmother's dramatic genius. I don't know where it had led her on this particular occasion, but the very evening of her departure my father brought another woman, whom he had found I don't know where, to the house. I can still see this creature, who was called Aline, a Swiss it seemed, who looked utterly bemused the first days. However, I very soon discovered I could not congratulate myself on her. Nearly every evening, when my father had left for the Comédie, she shut me up in the little maisonette where we lived in the Avenue de la République—where I was so frightened—to go and gad about, dressed in the most extraordinary white dresses, in some favourite Moulin-Rouge or other. For all that she would call me next morning 'Monsieur Paul' as formally as you please, it did not console me. Well, here was a new *ménage* which was not going too badly, when the absent mistress suddenly returned without warning. One night, about three o'clock, a cab stopped outside and someone cried 'Léautaud!' and shook the door. It was the actress come home, dissatisfied with the provincial theatre in which she had secured an engagement. Naturally, she had to be let in and you can imagine her surprise when, on reaching my father's room, she found his temporary mistress there. It all went off very well, however. There were screams from both sides, tears of course, and a few select insults, all of which went on for several days. Apart from myself, who took no interest in these things, my father was alone in preserving his calm. Knowing women as he did, he contented himself with locking up his medicine chest and his revolver and with taking his gun to pieces. Having done that, he had no further anxieties and, face to face with these two mistresses, who looked askance at each other, and each tried to persuade him to turn the other out, he soon decided what line to take. Since he could not dismiss the old one, who had a right of priority, nor turn the substitute out at the drop of a hat, since she was there only because he had brought her, he decided quite simply to keep them both, just like that, without another thought, come what might, as the gallant man he was! Who knows whether he was ever happier than at this time, with these two women sitting at his table when he came home to dinner and lying in his bed when he returned from the theatre? As far as I was concerned, the situation was tolerable enough. I was at last left in peace instead of being sent on errands all the time; I could attend to my own affairs and after dinner in the evenings I was no longer alone. Indeed, they were delightfully sociable, picking each other to pieces in the most charming way in the world! I had but one wish, that it might continue. Unfortunately, such unalloyed days could not last. After a few weeks, Aline left the house, yielding the place to her rival, and I had no resource but that of dreaming, without realising it, 'of couples who tarry forever', as M. Sully-Prudhomme so delicately has it. A little while afterwards, towards the end of 1884, my future stepmother was brought to bed of a boy. Thus my father had another son, and my life became even more like the old story I have indicated above, till the day I decided to get out, in about 1889. As for Aline, I was to see her again a few years later. One night, in 1895 or 1896, I met her in the Boulevard Rochechouart. She would certainly not have recognised me and she was much changed herself. But I never forget a face, and I knew it was her. I stopped her, and told her who I was, recalling one or two incidents to give her confidence. She told me several details about her liaison with my father, that she had been pregnant when she left the house, and that she had had a daughter a little while afterwards who had died a few years ago.

From time to time, my father had given her a little money for herself and the child, though only after repeated demands, and she had often had to wait for whole days on end under the theatre porch. And, indeed, I remembered having seen her once as I was coming out of the Comédie with my father, and that I dropped back for a moment on the pretence of reading a notice so as not to embarrass them. We talked of a thousand things. I can still see us walking slowly down the Rue Fontaine. What questions I wanted to ask her! She had never been a very pretty woman and was still less so that night. And yet, and I am not saying this to shock but simply because it's true, I believe, had I dared, I would have made her a certain proposal.

The best things come to an end, and I want to remind you of it here. Little by little, page is added to page, and these details, these charming family reminiscences become exhausted. A few more paragraphs, and they will be done; and then we shall get down to the quick of the subject, if the word is not too inappropriate as applied to a death. I repeat, you must reconcile yourself and not be too sad about it. Another time, I'll try to write at greater length. However, if I have no more to say, it's really my father's fault and none of mine. Since I was born when he was already thirty-eight, I know almost nothing about his early life. Besides, no man ever lived less at home. When he was in good health, I never saw him in the house except at meal-times, and in the morning when he got up; and thus all that part of his life he led outside the house is unknown to me also. His school of declamation, for instance. What charming particulars there must have been to note about his relations with his pupils, who were all young ladies! Whenever I went to see him giving lessons (in the morning, at his office at the Théâtre-Français), I always found one of them sitting on his knee. And, finally, I must add to everything else that he who was so gay and amusing, so it appears, outside his own home, never spoke at home at all, and never in any circumstances of himself. How can one write a complete biography under these conditions? I may even go so far as to say that there's considerable merit in what I've done, and that I deserve to be congratulated on my filial devotion which has always impelled me to make my personal reminiscences as complete as possible. You have seen my 'sources', as they say. In the first place, there was my Aunt Fanny, who used to come to spend a few days in Paris each year and took me about with her everywhere and whom for my amusement I used to make talk about my father. Then, when he retired from the Comédie, there were articles in the newspapers. And, finally, I had my mother's confidences at Calais during the course of our mutual effusions. My father was then still alive, and I had no idea that I would so soon be using what she, who knew him so well, told me. And less than three years later! I remember that, when I went to see him on my return from Calais and told him of Fanny's death, I said also that I had seen my mother again. 'Did she mention me?' he asked, rousing himself from his somnolence. Had she mentioned him! But I preferred not to answer and changed the conversation. And yet, I don't know why! . . . I see him still, sitting motionless in his arm-chair, before that picturesque landscape of a railway embankment where trains passed unceasingly, his head bowed, always silent, always unoccupied, and lonely too, perhaps? What a living example he was, there before my eyes, of La Rochefoucauld's Maxim CCCCXXIII! However, who knows? Perhaps he was thinking over his life, which had been so filled with tumbling women, and from which there now remained to him only this one very refined companion, a young son who liked sports and myself, who saw him so rarely? I remember he became almost shy of me. Perhaps I would have pleased him by talking a little more of the most charming of his women?

But, there it is, these fine sentiments are a bit late in the day. Nevertheless, I don't regret them. In the first place, they will give pleasure, as always! And, then, they will throw a little light on my relations with the deceased. It is true to say that at bottom I feel no greater resentment towards him than I do forgiveness! The two are equal and balance each other out into a great zero as far as he is concerned. Yet, I even go so far as to feel a certain gratitude to him, on occasion, when I'm feeling very particularly gay! My poor father, who seems at first sight to have done nothing for me! His 'manner' had a good side to it nevertheless, and I can but congratulate myself on it. 'I'll teach you to live,' he used to say to me from time to time. At that time, I did not understand, I was only a child. I concealed myself as best I could from his display of interest, whether in actions or in words, and hid myself quickly under some piece of furniture as soon as he came in; nor till I was sixteen did I feel anything but relief at his departure. Today, I realise that the gain is entirely mine. My mother herself, the eternally absolved, as I call her to myself, has by the very fact of her behaviour a right to my gratitude. In all conscience, would I be the man I am, if I had enjoyed a normal, respectable family life? Individual to the point of being disliked, free to the point of infuriating others, absurdly sensitive, unsatisfactory as it is possible to be, but very much myself, are fairly good results, so it seems to me. And if you come to think of it, I have no reason to complain even as an author. Can you see me with a properly married father and mother, who cuckolded each other mutually, and my having to relate it? I couldn't have done it. I should have been shocking the reader at every turn. While with a father and a mother like mine! . . . I don't want to over-emphasise this, it would be immodest and the advantages are so obviously apparent! Dear benefactors, indeed!

I remember, too, when we lived in the Rue des Martyrs or the Rue Rodier, when my old nurse was still with us, and he would take me into the prompter's box at the Comédie. Oh, what memories! We used to go by the Rue Fléchier, the Rue Peletier, the Passage des Princes, and that long Rue de Richelieu, which I was to love so much later on because of all the past. He seemed always to walk slowly, yet I had to hurry to keep up with him. How often we stopped at the tobacconist's at 62, Rue de Richelieu, while he went in to light a cigar, and I waited for him at the door! When we reached the theatre, we said good evening to Leclerc, the concierge, and then went upstairs. On the first floor, I said good evening to Picard, M. Perrin's commissionaire, then we went up to his office. He would collect his script, give it to me to carry to amuse me, while we went down again and I followed him on to the stage, where he talked for a moment or two with the actors, nearly all friends of his youth, while waiting for the first three knocks. It was there that I heard Céline Montaland say to him one day; 'Léautaud, you'll end up in prison because of the little girls.' We then both went to the prompter's box by the little staircase that led down to the first floor of the basement, leaving it at each interval to go and wander about the corridors backstage, or go to the greenroom, which was to the left behind the stage. On other occasions, I would go and sit in the stalls; the ushers all knew me and I was always given a seat. How long ago these evenings are! I have only memories of them now, but they are so vivid that a dress seen again, the intonation of a voice that has lingered on the ear, or the first notes of the overtures to certain pieces, are enough to carry me back as if they had taken place only yesterday. The theatrical tradition has grown no older, it is true. One might think one was still in 1880. They still play the same pieces, and even the actors seem the same under different names. The only difference is that at that time I enjoyed it. I can also still see the Comédie as it then was, with all the alcoves and recesses that have disappeared since the fire of 1900, and the actors who played there: MM. Barré, Garraud, Thiron, Laroche, Delaunay, Coquelin the elder, Fèbvre, Got, Boucher, and Mmes Madeleine Brohant, Sarah Bernhardt, Jouassain, Croizette, Bianca, Samary, Bartet, Tholer, Reichemberg. I'm not boasting when I say I was completely at home there, and that everyone was particularly kind to me. On occasion, an actress would take me to her dressing-room, and I would stay there for some time, enchanted by the scented coquetry surrounding me, while she changed her dress and renewed her make-up. How delighted I was when they played *Le Bourgeois Gentilhomme* and I could watch the little ballets of the tailor's boys and scullions to the music of Lulli! I already preferred light, lively, engaging things, the gaily sad, the unemphatically tender. My father would have liked me to be more serious-minded, and this sometimes divided us a little. For instance, he once tried to force me to appear in the children's scene in *Monsieur de Pourceaugnac*. He made quite a fuss about it. He had made up his mind, and spoke about it at home. I resisted as best I could, supported by my old nurse, who told him continually that he was wrong and that I should not enjoy it at all. When the day came, I besought him once more, tears in my eyes, to let me stay beside him. But it had no effect and I had to obey. Embarrassed and resentful, I had to play my part, which consisted in running on to the stage

with other children and shouting: 'Oh, Papa! Oh, Papa!'
Yes, indeed: Oh, Papa! But the worst of all till I was about
thirteen or fourteen were New Year's days. He would take
me to the theatre and oblige me, under threat of a box on
the ear, to go and wish a polite Happy New Year to various
actresses, practically all of them indeed. I don't want to
mention their names and I expect they have forgotten all
that. You can guess the reason for this. I acquired three or
four hundred francs by these compliments but he pocketed
them. How he made me suffer! But if anyone had told him
so, he would have burst out laughing. What a father! I ask
you! And now. . . . Oh, well, he's now at the bottom of a
regulation hole in that delightful cemetery at Courbevoie,
and I fear we're in danger of becoming sentimental.

For six years, he lived as I have described, almost
totally paralysed in his legs, scarcely able to move. At the
beginning, it was almost bearable. With an effort, he
could manage to go, from time to time, to his eternal café,
or walk a yard or two in his garden. But soon he was unable
to move, even to go from one room to another, without
the help of his wife or his young son, and was no more than
an old man, neither handsome nor ugly, sitting perpetually
in a rococo arm-chair. We had been living separately for
some fifteen years. I used to go and see him nearly every
fortnight, on Sundays, and spend three long desperately
boring hours, while he said not a word, for he was not going
to change his habits. What a fatigue these family obligations
are! I had already had enough of it by the time I reached
the Gare Saint-Lazare to catch my train in the morning.

It appears that on Thursday, 19th February, having got
out of bed during the night, he had fallen and been unable
to get up by himself. As it happened, my brother sauntered

in to see me next day. As usual, I asked him for news of his father, and he replied in very much the same terms as one might use to someone met in the street who happened to enquire. Happy age, in which the thought of the last leap is so far off that you do not even think of it in connection with others! But, the day after his visit, I received a letter from my stepmother. She blamed her son's casualness, told me my father was very ill and that I must come at once. It was the beginning of the end, as people say.

I therefore went. It was the morning of Sunday, 22nd February. I found my brother on the doorstep of the house in Courbevoie, he was on his way to send me a telegram. He said my father was dying. I went upstairs to my father's room. I must say, it was the sole occasion on which I enjoyed what might be called the prerogatives of an eldest son: as I went in, everyone made way for me. My father had not moved since they had picked him up the night before: his legs bent, one slightly over the other, his arms under the sheets, his face rather red and puffy, already much changed. I leaned over him, called his name, kissed him and spoke to him. He opened his eyes a little and looked at me; tears came to them, though he uttered not a word. Oh, he must have realised the moment had come, the dear man! Standing round the bed, my stepmother, my brother and I gazed at him not knowing what to do.

In the end, I sat down and opened the conversation. I learned that the doctor had been, had diagnosed various things, of which the clearest was that my father would never recover. My stepmother made a number of remarks concerning the sadness of the circumstances, a well-known repertory, and I agreed with much nodding of the head. As for my brother, he wandered restlessly in and out of every room in the house, like a young man who saw a fine Sunday for bicycling wasted.

Nothing very extraordinary happened during the rest of the day. My father remained in much the same state and I sat by his bed and kept him company. At this time, the paralysis that had seized on the whole right side of his body had moved no higher than his tongue, and my father was still perfectly conscious. From time to time, his wife, his son or I called his name and spoke to him, I don't really know why. We well knew that he was a man who never spoke anyway, and this was certainly no time to begin. . . . I would have given a lot, however, for him still to be able to talk and tell me what happy thoughts come to you when you lie there, so close to that last station to which the whole world comes. He was doing his best, what's more. Being unable to talk, he replied as best he could with a sort of low, weary inarticulate sound! It went on like this till evening. Then one of his oldest friends, perhaps the only one from whom life had not separated him forty years ago, came to see him and spoke to him. He recognised him by his voice.

At about ten o'clock, I went to Paris, then returned two hours later. My father was sleeping almost peacefully. Sitting by him with my stepmother, I waited for morning. I began thinking that it was not all that serious, that the doctor had exaggerated, etc. etc. But on the morning of Monday, at eleven o'clock, just as I was going to put on my hat and catch the train home, I asked my stepmother to open his eyes. She gently raised each lid in turn. The eyes were already veiled, almost fixed. I can see their sightlessness still. All the same! . . .

My peace was not to last long. That day of Monday and the night that followed were all. The next day, Tuesday, I had hardly got up when I received another telegram telling me to come at once. I had to go back to the station! But I was beginning to weary of it; the fortnights between my visits to my father seemed to be going pretty quickly. I had also just published *Le Petit Ami*, which had appeared eleven days before, and though I am not particularly enamoured of my writings, I nevertheless had other things on my mind than a preoccupation with death. 'God, why can't he die and leave us in peace?' I thought with a sigh as I entered the Avenue de l'Opéra, coming out of the Carrousel. To put a climax to my pleasure, this Tuesday on which I was taking the road to a doubly sad suburb was Shrove Tuesday. Indeed, it was so to an extreme degree, for the *Matin* was having a celebration or a centenary or something. It was barely eleven o'clock, and the Avenue de l'Opéra was already full of people who, when shut in their offices during the week, were no doubt all right, but really looked that day as if they were all wearing masks, for each was uglier than the next. Do what I would, all this had its reaction on me, and my normal capacity for emotion was affected by it. Shrove Tuesday! And that poor man out there was clearly not at all well! I had a note to write to the editor of the *Mercure*. I went into a post office. I told him of my circumstances and the duties which would undoubtedly keep me not only for that day, but very likely for others too. 'What an odd idea for Shrove Tuesday to be dressed in a winding sheet!' I added since the thought happened to cross my mind at the moment. One cannot always be ironical!

At last I reached Courbevoie. My father had not moved, but his breathing had become difficult, his face swollen and redder yet, while his forehead was burning hot. His heart was beating fit to break, so wildly you could hear it, and he had not opened his eyes since Sunday night. His mouth was already fixed in a curious grimace, the lower jaw twisted a little to one side! God really cannot be good-looking if you have to make a face like that when going into His presence. There could be no doubt of it, it was time I came.

Sitting at the foot of the bed, my right elbow leaning on it beside his bent legs, my head in my right hand, I resumed my position of the previous days. I have always rather enjoyed the circumstances of death and, if my visits to my father had often bored me, I was beginning to make up for it quite considerably now. His head was turned conveniently towards me, and I could contemplate him at my leisure. Oh, how I gazed and gazed at my dying father's face as it altered and spoiled beneath my eyes! It was like a need of my being and I think nothing in the world could have drawn me away from the sight. His breath was very much in keeping with the circumstances and almost suffocated me at times, in spite of the wide-open window behind me. But what did that matter! I beat the air with my hands, breathed a little ether, and it passed. I merely took advantage of the fact that I was on my feet to go nearer and lean over him the better to see him. Shall I ever forget that great head, still so live and so sad? It must be hoped so! Sometimes, too, I knelt at the head of the bed to see what his curious grimace looked like in profile. What a token of sympathy! I succeeded in imitating that grimace myself and, eight days after all was over, I still surprised it on my own face.

I went back to dine in Paris. It was even more Shrove Tuesday than in the morning, as you can imagine. What a contrast to the spectacle I had left! That poor man dying out there! How little the world cared! Wherever I went, I met bands of people laughing, singing, dancing, blinding each other with confetti. On the walls, the illustrated posters of the music-halls showed here and there pictures of gay women and old rips walking arm-in-arm beneath exciting titles. I could see afar off, on each side of the boulevards, the bright electric signs of the music-halls of my dreams. Oh, the crowds, the atmosphere of life and pleasure! I could not stop looking at it and I felt sobs mounting in my throat with a vengeance. Never more than on that night have I felt the sort of internal frenzy which sometimes makes me want to live my life to dance-tunes. 'Oh, laugh, laugh, go on, laugh then!' I thought to myself of the people who jostled me, and for two pins would have laughed too so near was I to its opposite.

Having returned to Courbevoie at about eleven o'clock, I spent the night watching with the same profit I have described above. My father was still stubbornly alive and the next day, Wednesday, in the morning, my stepmother and I sent for the doctor again to ask him what we had to expect. He saw at once that a change had taken place. The touching of an eye, the flicking of a muscle in the arm produced no reflexes. The brain had by now become affected and there was no sensation left. Only the heart was still beating furiously! There was nothing to do but wait, and not for long, he said.

Wait! Well, we could do that, indeed. We had been doing nothing else since the preceding Sunday, despite our devoted mien. We were doing so with a certain impatience even though we were not quite prepared to admit it. Since it had to finish thus, the earlier the better.

Besides, it's so true that one can get accustomed to anything! During the four days it had lasted, we had risen to the occasion, but time was passing all the same, with my step-mother at her housework, my brother at his office, and myself sitting comfortably beside my father, thinking already of these pages and making the best draft I could in my head. And then there was the usual performance, such as I had seen already in Calais at Fanny's death. People called for news and we had to ask them in. A quick glance at the patient, and then we sat round the bed and chatted. Of course, we talked a little of the dying man and of death, for the first quarter of an hour, but these eternal matters were very quickly exhausted, and we were soon talking of other things. Indeed, we even went so far as to laugh! What a lustre he then took on in my eyes, as he lay there, saying nothing, seeing nothing, his mouth just opening automatically under the pressure of his breath. Was that all the pain the living felt for the dead? Not even silence! It was not surprising he should grimace, and he would certainly have turned his face to the wall had he been able to do so, instead of keeping it turned towards us. Neverthe-less, if his breathing grew momentarily louder, or there were a wave of the stench that came from him, our attention would return to him. 'How long do you think he will last?' someone would ask with interest. Lord, how absurd one is for all one can do at such moments! As if it could serve a purpose, I felt obliged to rush forward, put my hand to my father's chest, apparently to determine the state of his heart, and then stand there, hand in air, without quite knowing what answer to make. Fortunately, the question would already have been forgotten; the conversation would have been resumed; and I was free to sit down again.

I remember a fragment of dialogue that took place before the announcements were sent out. Doubtless inspired by the spectacle, a thin wrinkled, elderly woman (Mme C———t) began saying how tired of life she was, how empty she found it, and that really. . . . 'Oh, no, indeed!' replied another, (Mme C———n), whose health and contours were both bursting. 'Since I'm here I'd as soon stay as long as possible.' Two schools of thought, as you can see. It was the latter, a very old friend of my father's, who found these splendid words of consolation: 'Bah!' she said at one point. 'He's had his share! He's had a lot of fun!' 'A lot of fun! Really!' I felt like replying. So it was such fun in his day, was it? Clearly, progress changes all!

Evening came at last, and we got rid of these people. We had dinner. I lingered a little at my father's bedside and, towards ten o'clock, I went with my brother to try to get a little sleep, leaving my stepmother to watch alone. But we couldn't sleep a wink; and, at eleven, we got up and my stepmother went to bed while we took her place for the night. The window was wide open in my father's room and it was so cold we could not stay there. We lit a fire in the kitchen and sat there, my brother and I, getting up in turn to go and see what was happening in my father's room. Since about four o'clock in the afternoon, my father had been dying more rapidly than ever. His breathing seemed to have disappeared or, rather, what one heard of it, was a harsh, monotonous, almost rhythmical little sound, something like the noise one's tongue makes clicking against the palate; yes, indeed, very like that. There were intermissions when it went slower, stopped almost completely and then began again more strongly, more jerkily. Indeed, there was nothing monotonous about it! His face was increasingly red, deformed and feverish, and his mouth's grimace more marked, while the heart continued its rapid beat. Well versed in poetry as I am, I remembered the alexandrine attributed to the dying Hugo: 'This is the battle-field, where day and night must fight.'

What a night it was! Trains passed continuously, whistling shrilly in the dark; our candles were always being half blown-out by the draught; we listened to the death rattle, as one listens to a clock striking the hour to count the strokes. In the end it all became more than was tolerable. As far as I was concerned, I could put up with it. But my brother! The time came soon enough when he was so affected, frightened almost, that he would no longer go into my father's room alone. So I let him stay where he was. I got up every ten minutes, went into the room, took the candle from the mantelpiece and, holding it close to my father's face, watched him dying a little more yet. I would most certainly have stayed there till the end, had the cold not become increasingly sharper and the stench worse. Since the afternoon, I had been assailed by a great pity and felt sorry for him with all my heart, that weak heart I have. It was so long since we had talked or shaken hands except automatically! It had already gone on for twenty years. And, really, how little he had loved me! I can remember no single kindly gesture except during the first seven or eight years of my life, when he used sometimes to take me on his knee, after meals, to fondle me and pinch my cheeks. How little he had known me! And yet, I was on the point of breaking down at that moment merely at the memory of those distant caresses he had lavished on the child I had been. Oh, I did not reproach him! This was not the time, and I had explained so many things to myself since then.

He had loved my mother very much. At that time, I was all that remained to him of her and, on the rare occasions he felt a little sentimental, he must no doubt have been moved to tenderness for the little boy, born of that beloved body. Then had come the day when he met the woman he was to marry in the end, my present stepmother. The image of my mother had faded a little, then even more as time went on, and so it had been with his feelings towards me, till the day came when he had another son by this other woman. The past had vanished altogether, and I no longer reminded him of anything at all, had become a mere embarrassment to his new liaison, to his present fatherly affection. All this was human enough and there was nothing to get angry about. So many people want the impossible! And how many other things I assessed while I was about it! He had asked that I be sent for, it appeared? . . . Yes, yes, it was agreed, all the past should be buried, as he would soon be himself! And we should talk of it no more. Besides, was I not there alone with him, as we had been in the past? . . . We had been so much apart. . . . And now it would be for good. . . . So my thoughts ran, and I was not too displeased with myself, despite my modesty. I remembered the distant years—oh, so distant!—when he took me for walks in Paris, holding my hand, he a florid old libertine, I a frightened little boy. The things he liked, his tastes, the few occasions on which I had seen him acting came back to me vividly enough. The first occasion was a long time ago, when I was a child, a matinée at the Cluny, where he had played in the *École des Femmes*, and another occasion, in a hall in the Rue Saint-Lazare, whose name escapes me. Then, much later, at Courbevoie, for charity, *Le Bonhomme Jadis* and *La Joie fait peur* with actors from the Comédie. He was a bit old-fashioned, like the rest of the illustrious cast, moreover, but what an easy natural bearing he had on the stage! He was really born for the theatre, and it was perhaps true that he was an excellent adviser in theatrical matters as I had so often heard it said. As for his tastes, the things he loved! He loved Racine, but he preferred Corneille and Molière. And the plays of Casimir Delavigne! 'No one writes plays like that today!' he once said to me, as we were coming out of a performance of *Louis XI*. How he hated new plays! I remember M. de Curel's dedication to him in a copy of *L'Amour brode*: 'To Léautaud, this soporific.' Significant enough! How he had bored me to death, too, when I was about fourteen, with *Le Chien du Louvre* by Casimir Delavigne, and *Jocelyn* by Lamartine, making me copy them out from sheer love of their verse! We had certainly not got on very well, either then or later. However, he had been happy, he had had simple tastes. Provided a piece had a patriotic tone he thought it admirable. Regiments, flags, parades, the little pieces of M. Déroulède or M. Manuel, and that exquisite *Marseillaise* filled him with joy. I thought with emotion that what he certainly regretted most, after women, was the 14th July.

Eventually, a moment came, a few minutes before two o'clock in the morning, as I was sitting in the kitchen by my dozing brother, when I thought I could no longer hear a sound from my father's room. I got up at once and went in. Oh, what a pretty memory for my collection! I saw my father raise his head, which he had not moved for over five days. I called my brother, who came running. We were both standing by the bed, at about the centre of it, quite close, and I was holding the light close to my father with my right hand. With his head raised, he uttered a great

'Ah!' It was hoarse and sounded strangled, then his head fell back. His face, which had changed so much these last days, to the point of becoming almost unrecognisable, suddenly, at that very instant, recovered, as if miraculously, its normal appearance. He at once raised his head again, made a face like someone about to sneeze, failed to do so, and let it fall back once more. Again he raised it, repeated the same grimace, finally managed to sneeze really quite loudly and for the last time let his head fall back. At the second time my brother fled, and I was so aghast that it needed all my curiosity to keep me there till the end. I went to wake my stepmother; she got up; and we all three went back to my father's room. He was still breathing very softly, and then his breathing stopped.

We then all three of us laid him out. I remember the weight of his head in the crook of my arm, when I raised him so that the sheet in which he was to be wrapped could be passed under him. 'This is what gave me life!' I thought, turning away a little so as not to look at him and avoid his face touching mine. 'Oh, seducer, what a reverse!' At the end of an hour, it was done, and more candles had been lit; we left him alone there in his room, and went into a neighbouring one to try to rest while waiting for day. But how can one sleep or be at peace, I ask you, when coming from such duties? Though my father was now at rest and walls separated us, I could still hear the sound of his breathing, that short, quick rattle, and the appalling stench was still in my nostrils. Lying uncomfortably on a bad bed, I could not take my eyes off the door of the room, so sure was I that it would open and I should see the dead man come slowly in with that handsome face of his I knew so well. The doors and windows rattled, shaken in their frames by the wind. Even the cat, under the bed, was washing itself and imitating unpleasantly the sounds of the agony that had now ceased. When would day come, and light, and life, so that I might leave, place a little distance between all this and me, turn to other things?

When morning came, we went to look at the dead man. His face had already turned very yellow, and become so hard and so cold! I touched his forehead. It was like touching a statue. And here is another affecting detail. A bandage we had tied round his head to keep his mouth shut had been put on so tightly that the pressure had made his nose curve a little and his cheeks become sunken, changing his whole appearance. 'You wouldn't think it was the same man!' said the people who came to see him. This was quite a consolation in itself! Then there was all the usual procedure. My first care was to write to my dearest mama. Oh, no fine phrases, simply two lines: 'Beloved Mother, my father died this morning at two o'clock.' How right I was, when I said Geneva was far away! I am still waiting for an answer. When everything was in order, I hurried back to Paris, for a moment's breathing-space and to see what was going on. He was put in his coffin the following morning and the funeral took place. I reached the house just as they were closing the coffin. As I came up, an undertaker, with charming thoughtfulness, pulled the shroud from the head so I might look at my father for the last time. I bowed my head a little to look at him. How quickly death had worked, and how much the face had already altered, the flesh fallen and withered, two great violet lines showing each side of the nose and under the eyes, while the stench, worse than ever now, rose up to meet me. I signed to them with my hand to hide it from me;

that it was all perfect. Alas, one never looks at the dead sufficiently. At the time, you are tired and nervous, fed up with the whole thing in fact. You feel no gratitude towards those functionaries who ask so politely: 'Do you wish to see him again?' You merely cast a hurried glance in order to have done. 'Take it away!' you would say almost, if you had not got yourself under control. But, afterwards, how you regret it and how you would like to have it all over again in order to see the dead once more! Regrets that begin as soon as the coffin is screwed down, and endure for all you can do, renewing themselves when you believe them extinct, even becoming an impossible obsession! I know about this, I can answer for it. So they fastened the coffin down, having placed between the dead man's hands a few flowers I had brought, without my taking any interest in the matter at all. Then he was taken downstairs. It was: '*Messieurs de la famille.*' And we set off. There was the devil of a wind, which blew my hair all over the place, and it was thus I led the procession, smoothing my hair down from time to time with one hand, while my other was burdened with my hat, and my ceremonious demeanour was constantly thrown into disarray. 'Poor boy, how distracted he looks!' people must have said, and with reason. Everything went off very well at the church, and no one recalled his virtues at the cemetery. By midday it was all over, and an hour later I was at home, hastily writing the essential notes. It was the 27th February.

What need be added to these noble words, as they say on tombs? I have nothing left of this man now but the memories I have so generously shared with the reader. One really has to write something from time to time and I have so little imagination! I also have his portrait, done when he was thirty, a large painting that used to hang over his bed, and which I took home, together with my sorrow, after the funeral. What pleasure that portrait gave me those first days! I hung it over a sofa, beside my bed, and every night, as I went to bed, still under the sway of the play I had seen and unable to help thinking of my father, it seemed to me that I saw him, there, in the shadows, lying beneath his portrait, a few feet from me, as I had seen him dying at Courbevoie, or dead, as I have described, with a chin-band holding his mouth shut. I could not even turn my face to the wall, so strong was the impression. 'Oh, they can be sure I shall send them the portrait back tomorrow,' I muttered irritably, thinking of my brother and stepmother. Naturally, I didn't do so and I don't regret it. I am quite calm again now and I think the picture looks rather well in my room.

Another enchantment, which is now beginning to fade, is the resemblance I see between myself and this man. To be free of so many things, and yet have these physical links with the dead man! I feel as if I were less I, less alone and less free. Some nights I think of it, as I lie dreaming before going to sleep. Lying in the position I saw him in, I screw my face into that dying grimace, with which I experimented so successfully, and, deny it as I will, our features are already so much alike, indeed at times my face wears an expression so like his, that the grimace might have been specially designed for me. Shall I die and grimace as lavishly as that? No, surely it's not possible? Mock as I will, it wouldn't suit me at all as a last facial expression!

Luckily, life goes on, with its movement, its excitement, its play of personalities and colours, the great race with its speed and its breakdowns. Merely a few months, and things are already better, and I hope the day will come when

I shall think of it no more. From time to time I go and visit his cemetery. I loiter a moment by the iron railing, trying to raise my interest. I notice how the earth has sunk still further, I calculate the time that has elapsed and think of all that must be going on down below, a few feet from me; perhaps the coffin has burst open, and he. . . . He must be in a fine state by now! To think that that body lived, moved, made love so brilliantly, that the mouth laughed with that laugh I hear again so clearly, that there were a few brains enclosed within that head, and that it is now all a dark, putrid mass—yet still so alive, but with what a life! I know I have already written something more or less like this in *Le Petit Ami*, concerning my celebrated Perruche. But is it my fault that I am continually losing someone dear to me? And here's another thing. A few details apart, these visits give one much the same feeling as visiting a hospital ward to see a patient. You come carrying flowers and looking rather foolish. There are people all over the place, sitting by the other beds. You stay a moment by your invalid, without doing much good or deriving much interest, looking about you to pass the time, and already impatient to get away. At last the moment comes when you can leave. 'Well, goodbye, I'll be seeing you again. Don't be too depressed. I'll be back!' And off you go with a great sigh of relief, turning round once or twice, nevertheless, to make a little signal of friendship.

Anyway, a truce to sentimentality, don't you think? My late father is not much to be pitied. It seems to me I have said enough about him in my works. You needn't laugh. It may even be very important. Indeed—am I wrong?—it seems to me these pages have considerable interest and that the reader is very much in luck.

PART III

Amours

————————————

Sleep, sleep, my dear loves . . .

PART III : AMOURS

I fell in love for the first time in 1888. It was at Courbevoie and towards the end of the year. For some time, about a year, I had been working in Paris, taking the train each morning and returning only in the evening for dinner. I was beginning to grow up. The story I have told about my trousers was some time ago now, and though I was not yet a dandy, I looked a little more respectable. Since my future stepmother was away on another theatrical tour, my life was somewhat easier. I had my own little room in the house where I had arranged a writing-table and a few books. I still had no idea of writing. Indeed, I do not think I had any ideas at all. I merely felt a certain pleasure at being by myself in my little room whenever I could, that is to say at night before going to bed, and on Sundays when I did not have to go to Paris. I had also largely recovered my freedom, since my father had never opposed my going out whenever I wanted to and for as long as I wanted to. He used to say as much even when I was ten. 'You have only to take the key; as long as you come home that's all that matters.' But Courbevoie! The good times of the Rue des Martyrs were over, the district had no attractions for me and I scarcely went out at all. I was not very sociable, had no need of society, was indeed still the same as I had been as a child. I had no companions even on my journeys to and fro between Paris and Courbevoie, and nearly always went to business and returned sitting scowling in a corner of the compartment. Besides, what companions I would have had! Old school-fellows become junior employees like myself, a band of young dolts who thought only of playing cards throughout the journey, each making more noise than the other. They had never liked me very much, precisely because of my aloofness, and I had always felt at a disadvantage with them owing to my shyness. I had had enough of them and did everything I could to avoid them. Nevertheless, I was not always successful in this, particularly later, after my military service, when I had gone home to live with my father and began working in Paris again. I had some very trying mornings at this period, when the whole band shouted after me all along that part of the Boulevard Haussmann which runs from the Rue Auber to the Chaussée d'Antin. There was absolutely no reason for it, of course. Since I did not know them, I ignored them, that was all. Really, if one had to know all the people one was at school or in the army with! One might as well know everyone with whom one has been in a 'bus! However, it seems that this is what morons, who like slapping each other on the back, call being stuck-up. I had chanced to see some of these louts on several occasions, when going to Courbevoie on Sundays from time to time during the last years of my father's life. Though I frequently passed them in the street, they did not recognise me; but I recognised them all right. Nor was this a matter for congratulation. That air of imbecility, which was so familiar to me when they were young, now distinguished them more than ever as men.

It was during these daily journeys that I made the acquaintance of Léon Ambert, the brother of my first mistress. To tell the truth, I knew him a little already. This dated back to the period of my last months at school. He was a friend of one of my school-fellows, called Chalgrain, and often came to meet him when we came out of school at four o'clock. I can still see him, as I used to see him then, far off in the vistas of the Rue de la Garenne, accompanied by a huge dog, a whip in his hand, gesticulating, talking and laughing loudly, cracking his whip and staring insolently at the passers-by. He lived in the Rue de la Station, which runs parallel to the railway and is crossed by the Rue de la Garenne by a little tunnel passing under the line. When he came to meet Chalgrain in the evening, they walked together as far as the corner of the two streets. It was the end of summer. Without seeming to, I used to manage to follow them at a little distance so I could watch Ambert filling the whole street with his voice and gestures. When they reached the corner of the Rue de la Station, they were often joined by a pretty girl with golden hair, an easy laugh and her neck and bosom somewhat *décolletée*, who seemed to have come to meet them. Chalgrain and Ambert would then say goodbye to each other, and Ambert would turn into the Rue de la Station with the pretty girl, while I went on my way, which was in the opposite direction. Had I been told then. . . .

Léon Ambert was just a year older than I, and was at that time a pupil at the School of Decorative Art, in the sculpture section. What a charming fellow he already was, so decorative himself and all too well aware of it, with his handsome head of hair that waved across his forehead like a woman's, his curled moustaches, and all his artistic swank and affectation. At the age one first begins to look about one, he had already seen everything, experienced everything and known everything, without of course being the least self-centred, since he was never happier than when he could find a listener to dazzle with his conversation. Furthermore, he was a perfect friend, blessed with the most delicate sensibility, always able to find some means of making use of you, as well as being prepared, from time to time, to do you a service for the mere pleasure of reminding you incessantly of it afterwards. I need add only that his qualities included the vanity of the devil and an already highly developed tendency to womanise, as well as an incipient, and no less irreproachable, absence of scruple, that was so natural to him one no longer paid any attention to it. He was still no more than eighteen but, if he were to be believed, no woman could help finding him irresistible and the number of his mistresses was already legion. Over and above all this, was the account he was prepared to give you of his family, all artists—and how talented!—and then, of course, there was the matter of art itself and his own genius. Oh, what lectures I had from him on art! I really believe it was he who disgusted me with that word for ever, as much as those who confect literary preciosities. He must have thought it showed great condescension—he, an artist, and I, a little employee!—but it made no difference, he told me about it just the same. I can see him, I can hear him still, developing endless theories, quoting the names of artists and their works, sculptures and sculptors, with, of course, his right thumb in the air, the other fingers closed, modelling incomparable forms in the void. With what quivering pride, what airs of assurance, what self-satisfaction he talked to me of what he wanted to do, of what indeed he would do! How happy his mother would then be, that admirable woman, as he told me continually, making a monstrous display of his veneration for her, so true is it that people who have mothers always take an unfair advantage of the fact. Nevertheless, you needed in particular to see and hear him in the subject of honour. Honour, his word of honour—perhaps I should spell it with a capital H?—was really the fellow's strongest point. He talked of it ceaselessly, tirelessly, in relation to the most futile as well as the most serious matters, and woe betide you if you laughed or dared even to smile. The mere idea of any possible failure in matters of honour infuriated him and, if you showed the slightest incredulity, his mind turned at once to the thought of a duel. What impressive manifestations of a spirit obsessed by the ideal! Listening to him made one think of knights of old for whom honour was more important than life itself. Unfortunately, our epoch is not conditioned to such high virtues. Indeed, so lively a sense of honour is apt to be misunderstood, and Ambert was to experience this a few years later, towards the middle of 1896. Having found a backer, he set himself up as a photographer, but owing to a somewhat frivolous attitude towards the accounts he landed in the police-court, while his partner, ruined and unhappy, blew his brains out. What a day it must have been, I mean for Ambert! It is true that he got off scot-free, thanks to certain string-pulling by his crazy mistress of the period, a young tart of forty, of whom I hope to say more at the appropriate time. All the same, after so many impressive protestations, so many fine speeches, hand to heart and eyes raised to heaven! They were as much moonshine as his desire to hear the whistle of a bullet. To think he was able to survive this misunderstanding! His sense of honour must have served him well that day.

But these compliments are premature in the chronological order of these reminiscences, and I must go back to my acquaintanceship with Ambert, which soon became a great friendship on both sides. A friendship that can be simply explained moreover. Ambert had an easy audience in me for his talking, lecturing and boasting. Far from bold or talkative myself, I was capable of listening, to him or another, for hours on end without uttering a single word, nor did it ever occur to me to contradict him or question his qualities. I was not then, as I am today, immediately aware of people's good qualities and filled with an irresistible urge to speak well of them. Qualities and defects were all the same to me: I paid but little attention to them. I lived, looked, listened, felt things vividly and remembered. For the rest, it was a question of waiting, and, as they say, no one has lost by it. Besides, how should I not have liked Ambert? He was always charming to me, an excellent companion, invariably gay, amused and amusing which, as far as I was concerned, was a change, like day is to night, both from my family circle and from my usual idiotic young companions. Perhaps ill-disposed people will say it was a blackguard charm? Lord, each to his own taste! Good people are usually so stupid and Ambert was not at all stupid under all his swagger. And, indeed, we spent many pleasant hours together at this period, took many pleasant walks, he boasting more than ever, and I happy to idle, feel free, look at things, forget my suburb and wander through districts I did not know. I was working at that time at La Nation Insurance Company at 1, Rue d'Amboise, which has since disappeared, in a little office in the entresol whose windows gave on to the street, and from which I could see reflected in the window-panes of the houses opposite the huge safes of the house of Fichet, then at the corner of the Rue de Richelieu and the Rue d'Amboise. I think it was in that little office I began observing the colleagues I have had in my various jobs. At first, I had as companions there a most distinguished old Italian called Rossi, who never said 'good morning' or 'good night' but 'buono giorno, mio caro' and 'a rivederci, Signor!' and from time to time swore 'cazzo di Cristo!' when his figures wouldn't come out. Then there was a nice, idle, witty sort of fellow, called Ternaux, who was always late, always in a good temper, and whose total effort consisted in sleeping all day over the piles of policies on his desk. The head clerk would wake him up from time to time. 'Really, M. Ternaux, what are you doing?' 'Me, Monsieur? . . . I'm waiting for six o'clock!' Ternaux would reply with a yawn. A third was called Lerouxel de le Vionnière, an impoverished aristocrat, who was in the habit of writing with huge cork pen-holders. He was short of a finger on the right hand, which embarrassed me every time I had to shake it. But the best of them all was our head clerk, M. Delorme, a tall fellow with a frank, open face, ex-cavalry officer and ex-man-about-town, who from time to time would talk of his memories of better times, leaning back in his chair, while we listened deferentially, smoking like chimneys. When the weather was fine and we were not particularly busy, he would send us out in turn for a stroll or to listen to the band at the Palais-Royal for an hour. As for me, I had special treatment from him. When M. Delorme saw me looking out of sorts in the morning, my eyes turned to the window, longing for the sunlight in the street, he knew what it meant: 'All right, Monsieur Léautaud, you want to go and see your friend in the Quartier Latin. Very well, off you go! You can come back after luncheon.' I didn't wait to be asked twice and went off as fast as my young legs could carry me. Sometimes I didn't even appear at all, or turned up only at eleven o'clock, having allowed Ambert to carry me off from the Gare Saint-Lazare. I had no difficulty in making my excuses to Mr. Delorme, who remained as amiable as ever. I frequently have an opportunity of remembering M. Delorme, who must have forgotten me after all this time. From time to time, I meet him about in Paris, walking whatever the weather, looking rather impoverished and somewhat older. I think of the blow it must have been to him when La Nation failed. He had a wife and child and it must have been impossible to find another job like that at his age. How I should like to stop him and shake his hand. 'Good morning Monsieur Delorme, don't you recognise me? Léautaud! You know, Léautaud, at La Nation?' But what would I say next? And he always seems in such a hurry. I have looked him straight in the face several times, and he has looked at me, too, but he hasn't recognised me. However, I must make up my mind to do it one day. I owe him that much.

The early days of my friendship with Ambert were spent as follows. When we reached Paris together in the morning, we used to meet one of his friends from the school at the station, a sculptor called Sonnette, and instead of going to my office I used to go off with them. We would go first to the School of Decorative Art for a little while, where Ambert and Sonnette moved a few lumps of clay about or attended half a lesson, then go off to the Luxembourg Museum to look at masterpieces, or sit in the Luxembourg gardens, or take long walks through the districts that lie between the Rue Monge and the Rue de Rennes, the quays

and the Boulevard Montparnasse. It was my first acquaintance with the left bank and those districts made no appeal
to me. As true friends, Ambert and Sonnette did their best
to sharpen my wits, as well as attend to my aesthetic
education. I stood so much in need of it, and though they
were such blades, they were such connoisseurs! But what
a waste of time it was! There was no sacred fire about me.
I was prepared to follow in their wake, imitate them, enjoy
their gaiety by laughing aloud at their traditional art-
students' jokes, but that was all. I had no desire to play an
active part. Nor was I any less of a blight in serious matters,
when it was a question of raising my mind to the pure
summits of art. I remember our visits to the Luxembourg
Museum and the first times I saw *Olympia*. Ambert and
Sonnette roared with laughter, were unable to find enough
sarcasms and insults to lavish on the picture and its school
of painting. 'Isn't that ugly and absurd enough for you ? . . .'
they said each time in an encouraging way. Ugly ? . . .
Absurd ? . . . I can still see myself gazing at it all by myself,
while they made their jokes. I am not saying that I could
already appreciate the whole beauty of *Olympia* nor that I
really understood it, but I understood still less why my two
artist friends guffawed so much. Then we would go on to
the works they admired, Falguière's nymphs and goddesses,
sculpture by Aimé Morot, a huge painting by Bouguereau,
called, I think *Mater Dolorosa*, and others of the same type
I have now forgotten. What praise, what emotion! Their
souls were in communion with genius, neither more nor
less. As for me, I hung about saying nothing as always,
clearly impervious to beauty for all the careful schooling
they had given me. What a wonderful thing it is to have a
feeling for art! Ambert finally became a provincial actor,

while Sonnette is sculpting the façades of houses today. Only I am still at it, and I have gone even further to the bad than in the days when *Olympia* vaguely attracted me and so many works of art made me yawn.

For some time, I desired no other advantages from Ambert's friendship. I knew he lived with his mother and sister at an uncle's, his mother's brother, a remarkable engineer, so he assured me. For, indeed, everything about him was so choice! They lived in the Rue de la Station, in a house set in a garden. Each morning, when our train passed the house, he pointed out his mother, that admirable woman, who waved goodbye to him from the threshold of her kitchen door, aureoled with a galaxy of saucepans. Sometimes, too, his sister appeared at a window, the first window on the right on the first floor, still half-dressed and also waving to him. She was the pretty girl with golden hair whom I had seen before. His father had left his mother many years earlier, when he and his sister were children. He was the son of an opera singer, who had enjoyed a certain celebrity in his time, and his two sisters had sung in comic opera, one of them, so it appeared, achieving real fame. In his youth, he had dreamed of a similar career, having a fine voice and, of course, astounding talent, but lack of money, getting married, children coming, etc. Ambert boasted continually of these glories and assured me that one day he would not fail to live up to them, very much the reverse, indeed. I knew so much then, but no more. And then one Sunday, when my father had forgotten to give anyone his free tickets for the Comédie-Française, it occurred to me to give Ambert a pleasant surprise. I asked my father for them and ran round to the Rue de la Station to suggest that my friend should go to the Comédie-Française that very evening. Ambert must have spoken of me, no doubt attributing to me qualities by the dozen out of pure habit, and they must have been expecting to meet me some time for they welcomed me warmly. Within an hour, I had made the acquaintance of his uncle, his aunt, their little girl and their son, who was about my age. There were also Ambert's grandmother, an elderly lady of the old school and extremely absent-minded, his mother, an excellent good woman, very stout and unsophisticated, rather like the old ladies in Ambigu plays, and, finally, Mlle Jeanne, a forthright young person who seemed to me to manage everybody, filling the house with her laughter, her voice, and the mass of her flaming hair. The tickets were accepted with pleasure, and I went off laden with invitations to come back whenever and as often as I pleased.

This is an opportunity of saying that, in all this story, I have always been the same in my friendships as in my love affairs: I have never made any pretence, nor ever tried to be more amiable than I can. The world is so odd, however, that I have always acquired, and to a considerable degree, the sympathy of anyone I have allowed to know me. It has often happened that I have been extremely surprised by this, having given it but little thought and taken but little trouble. Here's another who adores me, I think with a certain tenderness. We shall see if it lasts. And, naturally, I never expect it to come to an end, so true it is that habit becomes second nature. On the other hand, people who have met me only once or twice, or merely casually, are much more difficult, for they think me rude, shy and displeasing, in a word, someone to be avoided. Shall I cite the example of my mother, who has seen me for only eight days in her life? It has proved impossible to make myself appreciated by her, and each time we have seen each other, it has been merely to wait still longer before meeting again. This astonishing phenomenon occurred in all its stages with Ambert's uncle. The more I went there, the more I was invited to return, and I had been there but some five times when I was looked on already as a member of the household. I had, however, reason to suppose that they already knew something about me that first time, before they had ever actually seen me. It seems I had already quite a little reputation in Courbevoie. My father's house was considered a scene of the utmost depravity; he as a man who had whole relays of women in his bed, while I was supposed to sleep inevitably with all the maids. Inevitably! When I was indeed so very far from doing so at all, as you have seen. Unfortunately, the difficulties I had with my future stepmother were known also, and the charming life she led me and from which I was only just beginning to escape. This somewhat diminished my legend and my supposed frolics were given the less credence. Soon, indeed, they were looked on merely as gossip, and I appeared as I am, lacking in all prowess. I think that from the Sunday on which I took the tickets to Ambert, and even before my love affair began with his sister, I spent all my Sundays in that house. Everyone, even down to the uncle's small daughter, aged four, who asked for me throughout the whole week, was delighted to see me. I used to arrive about two o'clock and join the people who were calling. Ambert's uncle, that remarkable engineer, talked of his inventions, in which everybody showed as much intelligent interest as they could muster. I remember a Sunday, too, when a head of Mercury, sculpted by Ambert, was placed over the front-door. It is still there, even though other people are living in the house now; and in the days when I used still to go to Courbevoie from time to time, when my father was still alive, I looked at it each time I passed in the train. Then, when the callers had gone, we used to have dinner, just a family party, I sitting admirably placed between the two girls of the house, the little one and the big one; and then we used to stay chatting till about eleven o'clock. What did I say, what on earth did I talk about? I'm damned if I can remember! I simply let myself be adored, that was all.

The first moments of love that mark us so deeply! I try to recollect how my love affair with Jeanne Ambert began, and the extraordinary thing is that I remember so little. It must have begun two or three months after I first went to the house. Perhaps less. When happiness is in question, time is easily exaggerated. She had easy, forth-right manners, as I have said, was even rather tomboyish, and we soon became great friends. I was a bit of a change for her after the rather strait-laced people who surrounded her; with me she had no need to mind her p's and q's, which she detested. Indeed, the less she did mind them, the more she touched my heart. She used to join with me in playing with the uncle's little girl, and I would often find myself unexpectedly hiding in the same corner with her, while the child looked for us. Oh, the games of love and managed circumstance! At that time, there was really nothing of the seducer of girls about me, and it was she who began it, or at least encouraged me to it, by creating the occasions. Moreover, she was much more enterprising than I was. Besides, she was older. She was five years older than I. I was seventeen and she was therefore twenty-two. At that age she was a young woman and had her natural inclinations though, in fact, chaste. Moreover, she was very much taken with me, and did not conceal it, not enough, indeed, as I learned later, when her mother told me a few details about that time. In any case, I had no difficulty, we had traversed the road together, she indeed faster than I, and the day I began, she had been waiting already for some time. As for trying to paint her portrait, I find myself in a difficulty. Picture a tall girl of very striking appearance, with all the most voluptuous qualities, one of those women that make every man turn round, with the colouring and complexion of the auburn-haired when they are really pretty. And I may say without boasting that up till now most of my girls have been pretty. I still have a few photographs of her, taken at different periods while her beauty lasted, which was some ten years at most. One day—can one ever tell?—when we are all dead, perhaps these photographs will be found together with those of all the characters who appear in my memoirs, and they will be published. People will see then if I was right. A pretty woman for a mother, a pretty girl for a first mistress! These things can sometimes adorn one's dreams for life. I am searching again, as I said above, for the beginnings of our love affair and still can find nothing very precise, unless it be the following. One Sunday, I had gone to Paris in the afternoon. It had been agreed that I should come back to dine in the Rue de la Station. When I arrived, she was standing on the threshold of the street-door. I had bought a bunch of violets for her. Finding her there alone in the evening dusk, I gave them to her. She pretended to be surprised, I remember, and I then said, with my usual amiability, those sweet words she had been waiting for and had done everything to encourage.

Then, what a romance began; it will certainly require quite a number of pages from me, without counting the emotion! From then on, I was always at the Rue de la Station, not on Sundays only but nearly every evening too. Jeanne knew so well how to encourage everyone to invite me, without seeming to, and I had such good reasons for going there myself! Was not this pretty girl my whole life? At least, I told myself so and with complete conviction. I spent every week-day waiting impatiently for the moment I should see her in the evening, and the whole week sighing for the joys of Sunday, and she for her part did so too. How all this failed to awaken the suspicions of the uncle and aunt sooner than it did was really one of those rare pieces of luck. However, Jeanne managed everything and I placed myself completely in her hands. When I arrived on Sundays, I spent but little time in the uncle's study listening to him talk about his work. These great matters no longer interested me, and I much preferred going into another room with Jeanne, in the company, which mattered but very little, of her mother and grandmother. There, we played games, chatted and devoted ourselves to our love. There was a musical-box we used to play quite a lot to amuse ourselves: *La Gavotte Stéphanie*, *La Dernière Pensée de Weber*, *La Promenade sur l'eau*, and other tunes whose names I have forgotten, which were accompanied by a continuous little metallic sound. How delightful it was! It was at this time Jeanne gave me her picture, a photograph, the first I ever had of her and still possess. This photograph was already rather old, dating from when she was seventeen or eighteen and still lived in the Rue Lamarck, where she had been born, and showed her rather chubby, with masses of hair down to her eyes, as was then still the fashion. But what pleasure it gave me all the same! She had written a dedication on the back: *A souvenir from his beloved to her darling Paul. Given the 14th April 1889. Love and Fidelity. Jane.* 14th April, 1889! Seventeen! Ah, youth! When I read those adorable lines today, they seem to me as absurd as an inscription on a tombstone. Nevertheless, love had lent me inspiration too, I must admit. I had left my job in Paris—I had been rather too witty with the chief accountant of *La Nation*—and I was temporarily employed in Courbevoie itself on a little local paper where I had nothing to do. While there, I remember, I wrote a few verses for my idol of which the songs of M. Xavier Privas would give a fairly good idea, were they not even more ridiculous still. Fortunately, my shyness in this matter saved me, and their object never knew anything of these masterpieces, no more than I know what I have done with them. But these hours of poetic composition were soon curtailed. I found another job in Paris, at 11, Rue de la Grange-Batelière, with a sort of knight of industry and my journeys with Ambert began again. How much better off the world would be if every girl had a brother like Ambert; my love for his sister had but increased our friendship. Since they concealed nothing from each other, she had told him about it the very first day, reminding him that she was his elder and that it was not his place to mention it to anyone. But this was to insult his noble heart. Ambert had too much need of his sister on his own account to say anything at all and, on the contrary, he helped us as best he could. For instance, it was he who delivered the letters Jeanne and I wrote to each other, since we were not content with merely seeing each other every day. One has so much to say when one is in love, and such intelligent things into the bargain that they can only be written! The great friendship of the son and the flattering love of the daughter had earned me the mother's goodwill, and I was beginning to believe that she was an admirable woman enough. Every morning, I left my father's house some little time before the train was due, and hurried round to fetch Ambert. No one in the house was yet up, except he and his mother, who was always inclined to spoil him. A comfortable breakfast was ready: I had my share of it and we then left together. When the train passed, taking us to Paris, there was no need for either of us to be jealous, since we each had a distant wave, Jeanne's for me, for she jumped out of bed and ran to her window for the purpose, and his mother's for Ambert. When I returned in the evening, I went to the Rue de la Station before going home. Jeanne would be waiting for me at the door, tender and vital, and we would remain there together for several minutes, while Ambert kept the family talking inside, or took the dog for a walk along the railway embankment, deliberately making a great noise of talking and laughing so that no one should think of coming out to see what was going on. Nor must I forget the evenings spent at the uncle's house, which often ended these days. What sweet hours they were! I either went to dinner or arrived soon afterwards. The uncle went back to his study. Ambert was out more often than not, having returned to Paris for a lecture or to go out on the town. As we sat round the big table in the dining-room, we consisted only of the uncle's wife and son, the grandmother and Ambert's mother, Jeanne and myself. We drank tea, chatted or played lotto. Oh, the first pressures of the hand of the woman one loves! Pressures I reciprocated. Jeanne always sat beside me, and when the game had got properly under way, she would slip her hand beneath the table and remain thus throughout the game. It was she who had thought of this, the dear angel, and how right she was. From time to time she would amend her demeanour and then begin again. I can still hear her laughing at the blindness of the others who were thinking of nothing but their counters. Indeed, these good people suspected nothing, but suppose they had found us out! Can you see me, in particular, with everything discovered? But how could they, when the grandmother was half blind, the mother blind in another fashion, her son and daughter doing just as they liked, and the uncle's son not caring a damn anyway? There was no danger; and if they had seen us they wouldn't have said anything. As for the aunt, Jeanne always managed so cleverly to make her sit as far away from us as possible! I also remember very well one evening before dinner in the hall of the house. We were going from the uncle's study to the dining-room. We were the last. Jeanne went out ahead of me, then stopped in the hall, which was unlit, in a sort of alcove, made by the staircase leading up to the first floor. I came out in my turn and was going past without seeing her when she took me by the arm and drew me to her in an embrace, and there, in one minute. . . . Another evening, I had come, as usual, to the street door to give her a kiss. She took me by the hand and led me into the garden, going round the house. The house was divided on the ground floor by a passage which formed the hall and had two doors leading into the garden, one at the front, the other at the back. She led me silently in through the back door, through the hall, up the little staircase to the first floor, and into her bedroom, which I now entered for the first time. There was no light. Below, the whole family was at dinner, as sedate as so many Baptists. Jeanne went down for a short while, dined quickly, and then returned to me. For the first time, I found myself really alone with her, held her abandoned in my arms and touched with my hands her almost naked body beneath her dressing-gown. What a delicious, unforgettable moment, and what an opportunity! My fair friend had certainly expected excellent results from this secret meeting. Her bed stood there ready. We were even sitting on it, if I remember right. But I did not know, I did not think of it, at least, I don't really know what I did think of, perhaps it was the lack of security? And nothing passed between us but kisses. I remained there about an hour. Then as a favourable opportunity came to leave, I went out in the same way and by the same route, Jeanne guiding me in the dark, both of us being as silent as we knew how. To all intents and purposes, another failure when I come to think of it.

We used also to go and bill and coo out of doors from time to time; and you will see that if Ambert helped our love-affair in the most friendly way, he also on occasion derived advantages of his own from it. At this time, there lived at Courbevoie, in the Rue de Normandy, quite close to my father's, but in a somewhat isolated little house, for that particular district was sparsely built over, a lady called Lefébure and her two daughters, one aged about twenty, the other thirteen or fourteen. There all the young coxcombs of Courbevoie gathered every evening, assiduous in their attentions to the mother and the elder daughter, while the younger daughter served more or less as a maid. Mme Lefébure was still young, and seemed even younger than she was, though only from a distance, it is true, and then owing to her youthful dresses and affected behaviour; but there was not much difference in appearance between her and her daughter, since they were both slim and as affected and risqué in their manners as each other. They both appeared nearly every year in the amateur theatricals at Courbevoie. I remember seeing them once or twice, looking foolish and awkward, singing songs that might have been written for them in rasping voices. They reminded me of my future stepmother at the period she used to make the same sort of exhibition of herself in similar theatricals. As for the husband and father, he didn't bother them. He was a commercial traveller, it seemed, or something of the sort. Each month, he used to come back to his wife in the middle of the night and then leave at dawn again to continue his itinerant existence. At least, this was the picture the mother and daughter drew of him for their young adorers, who were, I repeat, numerous. Just think of it! Two actresses, neither of them unforthcoming, with all the charms of talent and physical accessibility, for you could have the mother in the daughter's absence, the daughter in the mother's, if not both of them! For these young men it was a bit of cheap skirt, and the house was often full till very late at night. And Ambert would not have been Ambert if he had not endeavoured to exercise his talents as a womaniser there. Which of the two he was courting, the mother or the daughter, I never knew. I dare say it made but little difference to him. He wanted merely to have one of them in order to be able to boast about it afterwards, and no doubt pursued both at once. Besides, with his attractiveness and his profound knowledge of how to talk and make love to women, he was perfectly sure that they would both fall into his arms. His one difficulty was to be able to go there every night, so as to be certain of achieving his conquest. As if it were an intervention of fate, it was precisely in the evenings he was least free, since his uncle didn't like him to go out after dinner. When he wanted to spend an evening in Paris, he could give the pretext of a lecture, which was fairly well received. But in Courbevoie itself what pretext could he give, and one moreover which would cover several evenings? In face of my love-affair with his sister, he soon found one. Summer was beginning. Going for a walk in the evening after dinner was already becoming feasible. It would make an excellent excuse for going out. He had but to make an arrangement with Jeanne. Brother and sister going out together could arouse no suspicions. He therefore came to an understanding with her. Would she not enjoy a little walk with me, while he went and had fun in the Rue de Normandy? It was so obvious, she agreed at once and the outings were organised. Practically every evening for a whole fortnight, either Jeanne or Ambert talked casually, after dinner, of going out for a little stroll, merely for a breath of fresh air. The other said yes at once, or pretended not to be very keen about it, the better to put everyone on the wrong scent, only to acquiesce in the end, as though to please the uncle, who looked on these outings as so natural that he was the first to encourage them, going so far even as to reprimand whichever of them was being lazy, so that in the end they went off arm in arm, looking as unhurried as if they were going nowhere in particular. We used to meet at the corner of the street; and Ambert rushed off to his women, while Jeanne and I went for a walk in that ravishing Courbevoie country, out beyond the last houses, more often than not along the railway embankment, and then by the highway called the Havre road. Having found a quiet corner where we could sit comfortably, we remained there half an hour or an hour, according to the time we had at our disposal. And the caresses, the sweet manual games we practised under the table during those evenings at the uncle's house, were now given a free run. Here both Jeanne and I were at our ease, and trousers were soon unbuttoned and skirts quickly raised. And yet what chastity—relative, if you like—we preserved! We indulged in a somewhat lively mutual masturbation, but that was all. Those moments are no longer very present to my memory, or at least my sensations are not. No doubt, our imaginations ranged no further than these games, for I did not dare, and she, though she must have thought about it much, had clearly certain hesitations in face of the ultimate decision. I remember one of these evenings more particularly. We had gone in an entirely different direction that night and had sat down in a little wood, called Kilford Wood, off the Kilford road, merely the other side of the railway embankment from the uncle's house. No one could have seen us even in broad daylight, for we were well concealed in a copse. I kissed her and caressed her and then. . . . What delicious and delightful walks they were in which our young hearts beat so much in unison. And then we would all three meet at the agreed place, and Ambert and Jeanne would go back to the Rue de la Station together, as casually as they had left it, an innocent brother and sister, who had merely taken a little constitutional together.

Ambert was a very different sort of chap from me. Not only did he make love properly—and he was certainly right as far as that goes—whereas I was rather backward, but he made it in several places; the Lefébure ladies never made him forget his friends in Paris. It was concerning one of these that, when we had all three met one night, he made the following proposition: 'I should like to spend an evening in Paris with a woman I know and take her to the theatre. If you will, you might give me tickets for the Comédie and bring them to the house as if of your own volition. I'll pretend to make arrangements to go with Jeanne. We'll say we're going together, and you can meet us in Paris. Then Jeanne can spend the whole evening with you, and we can meet again after the theatre and all take the train home together.' Everyone must agree that Ambert was charming to me: he was asking me to look after his sister for an evening, while he spent a few hours with his mistress. I really could do no other than accede to his wishes, and that was what I did: I accepted. At this distance in time, there are a number of serious reflections I can make about this proposal. It was all a little equivocal. Brother and sister had doubtless come to an understanding. It may even have been Jeanne who first had this excellent idea and had persuaded Ambert to it by pointing out all the benefits he would derive from it himself? She must have known so well that one could obtain anything from him provided it served his interests even to the smallest extent. So what? Honest love, pure love, are they not the contrary of love? One does the best one can. Even if these moral idiocies had occurred to me, they would not have stopped me, I am quite sure of that. I had lived so much amid equivocation throughout my whole liaison with Jeanne, and with other people who lived in the same way, without ever being embarrassed! It is true that it did not occur to me, and that was my one fault. Today, I would derive an added pleasure from it.

I therefore asked my father for tickets and Ambert and I arranged our rendezvous. I was working at that time, as I have said, at 11, Rue de la Grange-Batelière. In passing,

I remember it was in that office that a young journalist, whom I had for colleague, thought I had such an aptitude for political economy and was so persuasive that at the time I was telling everybody I was going to take it up. Ambert's uncle, who thought I had talents as an orator, considered it a splendid idea. It was also while I was in this job that Ambert persuaded me into a business that could have caused me a lot of trouble. He told me some story, which I cannot now remember, of why he had to have fifty francs absolutely at once. Fifty francs was quite a lot of money to me and I had nothing approaching that sum. I therefore bethought myself that my father had a wine-merchant in Courbevoie by the Church, who sometimes cashed IOU's for him when he needed money. I had often been sent on these errands. It was a means! I suggested it to Ambert, and he swore by all the gods that he would have the money in hand when payment fell due; I therefore wrote out an IOU at a month's date, as my father did, and took it to the wine-merchant, who cashed it without even looking at it. Naturally, on the eve of its falling due, Ambert had not a penny, and it was essential to go and pay the following day to prevent the IOU being presented and my father getting to know of it. Ambert was quite happy merely to despair, and did nothing to get me out of the mess; in his heart of heart's he probably did not care a rap. But I was in a tight corner. It was then I had the idea of writing to my godmother, Bianca, whom I had not seen for years, not since the departure of my old nurse, who used to take me to see her on Sundays, such delightful and too short days. I explained my difficulty very frankly to her, and she responded at once. The very next day, her companion came to see me at my office. She gave me the fifty francs, and I was able to go that very evening to recover the IOU and rid myself of my nightmare. I was so thoughtless I forgot to write and thank her, which has created a coolness between us ever since, to my great regret. But I must return to our evening out. The day before I had gone to the Rue des Martyrs, to the Hôtel des Martyrs, which was in the house that today still bears the No. 7. There, in the old days, had been the Brasserie des Martyrs, which I had known a little in my childhood. The hotel of which I am speaking disappeared itself a few years ago, and the whole house is now occupied by a draper's shop with the name of Galerie des Martyrs. I had booked a room, in which dinner was to be served, for the next evening, paying in advance something like twenty-five francs, I think. I had no cause for complaint, moreover, it was very well done. At six o'clock, Ambert brought Jeanne to me at the Rue de la Grange-Batelière and, confiding her to my care, dashed off to his assignation, while we went to the Rue des Martyrs. Did Jeanne sometimes remember that evening spent in that pretty room hung with blue hangings, a really feminine room, which I recollect so clearly down to the last detail, when she lived in that district with her husband, in about 1900 to 1902? Indeed, it's a happy memory, particularly for a first assignation. But in spite of all our splendid arrangements, I was once again as I had been with the maid of whom I have spoken, lacking in skill and enterprise. Besides, the two occasions were so close to each other. Only a few months apart, certainly. There was also on Jeanne's side an overwhelming difficulty which, at each attempt, caused her more fear than pleasure, so that in the end we were limited to our usual exercises, though on a greater scale, that was all. The time passed quickly, moreover, soon eleven o'clock struck, and we had to get up and dress to go back to our suburb. I can still see Jeanne, just as we were leaving, making a clean sweep of all the candle-ends left from the party that she might read secretly in her room at night, she said. When we reached the Place de la Trinité, where we had agreed to meet in a little white café which is still on the corner of the Chaussée d'Antin, Ambert was already waiting for us, and we all three hurried off to the station. On the platform, I found my father, also on his way home, and, when I had introduced Ambert and his sister, we all got into the train together. It was written that Ambert should have all the pleasure of the evening for himself. Sitting opposite my father, he never stopped talking throughout the whole journey. A man of the theatre! What an opportunity to boast! The whole family was mentioned, the grandfather opera singer, the two aunts who sang in comic opera, the engineer uncle and his admirable mother, after which he got down to his own qualities, talents and future fame. My father was always in excellent humour with other people! He had known the two singers very well. He chatted with Ambert most cordially. As for Jeanne and I, though we laughed from time to time, we hardly spoke, merely enough for politeness' sake. Perhaps she was thinking of the evening we had spent together, and that when all was said and done she had got no further forward, poor dear. As for me, I was probably concerned with a still graver matter. Were we not going to have to part till tomorrow? When you are in love, the least separation is such a wrench! But everyone knows that, I need not emphasise it.

It was only a short time after that evening that I became an employee of the newspaper *La République Française*, at

216

42, Rue de la Chaussée-d'Antin, a publication which, as one knows, thrives on not being known. If I am not mistaken, it was towards the end of the Boulangiste period. I knew there, more or less, several people famous for a variety of reasons, whose names, if carefully selected, will not come in badly here. To begin with, the editor of the paper at that time, M. Joseph Reinach, whose work is so amusing, and to whom I acted in the capacity of secretary on two or three occasions. Then Jules Ferry, whom I remember clearly as he climbed the stairs leading to the editor's office, his back bent, his eyes moving timorously from side to side as if he were always in fear of something behind him. And then M. Eugène Pitou, chief of the editorial staff, on whom the concierge doted, as one could see from the way she ran out and stood in the courtyard, turned suddenly into a veritable statue of admiration, each time he passed. Then there was Mme Jeanne de la Vaudère, who had just made a start in literature with a novel which was serialised in the paper, and which I read no more than I have read all the others she has published since. Finally, I will present M. Friedmann, the cashier and manager, a tall, gaunt Alsatian, who was gruff and hasty but had a kind heart. M. Friedmann lived in Courbevoie as I did, knew my father well, and all about my charming family circumstances. And, indeed, my future stepmother had come back from her tour, the last and most fruitful, for she had brought back a child, as I have said, and my good times had begun all over again. There was no question of the pretty tricks of the past, they were no longer in season. But to see me going out every night, paying no attention to her or her protests, infuriated her and she was constantly picking quarrels with me. The great pity of it was that my father, with whom I had got on pretty well while she was delighting the provinces, turned against me again after she came back. A first breach quickly resulted, and the story of it will add to my collection of paternal anecdotes, so different, and I do not regret it, from those of M. Claretie. Each day a similar quantity of white and brown bread was delivered to the house. The first was for us, the second for the dogs. The trouble was, however, that both my father and my future stepmother were so fond of the second, that the procedure was reversed. The brown was kept for the table, and the white given to the dogs. But I was not altogether in agreement on this point with my family. I hated the brown and was always asking that some of the white be kept for me. Surely I was not exacting in asking to be treated like a dog? Naturally, since my father did not concern himself with such things, I addressed my requests to his gracious mistress, but all she replied—and in what select terms!—was that if I was discontented I could clear out, that they would both be delighted, my father most of all. I was certainly often discontented but, as to clearing out, wait a minute! Anything she said on that score meant nothing, and I didn't conceal it from her. It was as much my home as it was hers, indeed even more so, and I had heard my father make this impressive announcement one day when they were having a row about me. If someone was to tell me to clear out, it was not she, and as for my father, the day he told me to go, I would know how to deal with him by myself. But one fine day it happened, or one fine night, rather. He did not have to go to the theatre, and we were dining together. Moreover, these were the only nights on which I had a proper dinner. On the others, when he dined at six o'clock and then left for the Comédie, the table had been cleared by the time I got home, my future stepmother had gone out to call on gossips in the neighbourhood, and I had to dine as best I could. The excellent man was therefore present, as was the brown bread, which was served me once again. Since I had now been complaining for some time past, I could stand it no longer and, kicking over the traces, I may possibly have failed to conceal what I felt about her obstinacy. Whether it was that he was in a bad humour, or that his mistress had put him up to it, my behaviour aroused my father's rage, and when that man was in a rage he was worth seeing. 'If you're discontented,' he said, 'you can go to eat elsewhere and clear out!' The same phrase that she had used! They were clearly twin souls! I determined at once to leave them to their happiness. Dinner over, I was left alone, while they went for a walk in Courbevoie. It was the moment, if ever, to immolate myself. I took a little trunk from the attic; it had once served my father when he used to play in the provinces. I put my things in it and, locking the door behind me, without paying any attention to what the neighbours might think, went and took the train to Paris. I had precisely ten francs in my pocket! When I arrived in Paris, I drove in a cab to the Rue Monsieur-le-Prince, where I took a room in a hotel at random; it was at No. 45, then the Hôtel de la Lozère, today the Hôtel des Charentes; those people don't look at one too closely. Oh, that little room next to the lavatory in the cheap students' hostelry, and that first evening of independence! Not one of my happier memories. To think there are people who actually live in such places. I went out again at once, and spent the rest of the evening considering my unhappy situation on the terrace of a café which is still at the corner of the Rue Monsieur-le-Prince and the

Boulevard Saint-Michel—the one where you have to go down a few steps—and went back to the hotel only to go to bed, as I did every night I stayed there. As soon as I reached the office next morning, I told M. Friedmann of my change of abode and what had led up to it. He approved at once, and supported his approval with an advance of salary so that I could manage. I lived quietly at the hotel for two or three days, and then my father made a move. He, who never wrote, began by writing and ordering me home. He excelled in giving orders, that man. But he was less good at understanding. Then he complained of my departure to M. Friedmann. He was well received. 'My dear friend,' said the kindly Alsatian, 'I'm on your son's side, and not only I. However, I'm prepared to act as an intermediary to persuade him to go home. But on one condition only. You will give me your word of honour not to say a word to him about his leaving nor of the money he has spent.' It was written that I should not yet be left in peace. In an access of love for me, my father gave his word; M. Friedmann deployed his diplomacy; and, at the end of a week, I reappeared among my delightful family, who welcomed me home. But the spell was broken, and the evil day was only postponed.

Moreover, life was going no better in the Rue de la Station, in the house of my love. The aunt, a little, dark, rather ugly woman, was very jealous of Jeanne and since, so it appeared, she had at last discovered our love-affair, there had been something of a scene. Mme Ambert, the good soul, trying to smooth things over, had succeeded merely in increasing the discord and being accused of wilful blindness. All this was told me one evening, when we had gone for a stroll, Jeanne, Ambert, their mother and I, and I was advised to come less frequently to the house till things got better. Ambert even seized the opportunity of explaining to us the real basis of the aunt's anger, for which my intimacy with Jeanne had been no more than a pretext. The real truth of the matter was that the woman was madly in love with him, which was pretty obvious, wasn't it? Indeed, had he wanted to sleep with her! . . . But a fat lot of chance she had with a chap like him! Upon which Mme Ambert gazed tenderly at him, approving him with as arch an expression as she could muster. Discord in the house soon became accentuated, everyone playing their part, from the angry aunt to Ambert and Jeanne, who were far from displeased at the possibility of achieving freedom, while the uncle's son was much amused by the whole thing. The house became an inferno, family life a memory. Mme Ambert had to resign herself to leaving her remarkable brother and going to live in Paris with her children. The evening I heard the news was a good one. But for all her stoutness, Mme Ambert kept wavering, while her son and daughter praised her continually, for fear she should change her mind. Ambert did not come home for three days, busy, so it appeared, searching for a lodging in the neighbourhood of his school. Then it was a question merely of organising their departure and their incredible number of packages, and of saying goodbye.

It seems to me that it was now that the meeting took place at which Jeanne and I repaired our bad behaviour of the Rue des Martyrs. It may have occurred only after their departure from Courbevoie, but in that case it must have been at the very start of their coming to live in Paris, and I shall be out by only a few days. We had arranged to meet on the Place du Palais-Royal, one afternoon, at three o'clock, and the ceremony took place in a hotel room at 4, Rue de Vaugirard, the Hôtel de Lisbonne this time, whose appearance I remember very well. I was wonderfully naïve on going in. I remember showing the waiter the little brief-case, full of papers and books, I always carried about with me at that time, feeling the need to tell him I had come there to work and asking him to send up writing materials, all this to allay the shyness from which I suffered. I really ought to have taken a few notes, as I have always done since, even in less serious circumstances, such as my father's death for instance, or the meeting with my mother at Calais. I should at least be able to write a few good lines at this point. Indeed, my memories of this great day on which I first made proper love to Jeanne stop here. It is not even worth my while to seek further. I can see again that pale rose body, those full, firm breasts, that face bright with ardour, and other still more interesting beauties; I breathe the auburn odour of her hair and body, but as to the details, my own pleasure and ardour. . . . They are no more present to me than if someone else were in question. Is this perhaps due to the emotion inseparable from a first time?

The day came at last. It was in the first half of 1889, probably the end of May or the beginning of June. The Universal Exhibition had been open only for a short while. Ambert, his mother and Jeanne went to live in a little flat in a rather sordid house, miles away from my usual district, high up in the Faubourg Saint-Jacques, at No. 13. I was told as soon as they had moved in, and went to have a look. I still remember how very far away I thought it was that first time. From then on, I spent all my Sundays there. I used to leave Courbevoie early, go first to *La République Française* for the Sunday mail, then go on to the Faubourg Saint-Jacques, either on foot, or on the top of the Montmartre-Place Saint-Jacques omnibus, which has not been running for some years now. The house, which has since been pulled down, stood a little forward from the alignment of the street, and as soon as I reached the last houses in the Rue Saint-Jacques, I could see far off, beyond the crossing of the Boulevard de Port-Royal, at the window of the flat, a dear, auburn head (old-fashioned style) watching for my arrival. It was between nine and half past. Mme Ambert was either marketing or set out as soon as I arrived. Jeanne was just sufficiently dressed to delight me, and we had an agreeable moment of intimacy, of tenderness and—for I can indeed write the word—of youth. How vividly I remember those mornings! I can still feel the bright warmth of the sunshine of those days, and that's a pretty detail, is it not? At the start, as you look life in the face, everything seems so wonderful! And you are so soon disillusioned! You merely go on, deriving what pleasure from it you can, for its novelty and freshness have worn off. Since they had left Courbevoie, Ambert was no longer living with his mother. He came merely to spend the night from time to time, or to visit her during the day, to give her his news. At the very time of the move, he had met his father in the street one day, either by chance or because he had set about finding him. The son of the opera singer, the brother of the two comic opera singers, the one time candidate for a musical career, having worked for a time in a soap factory, had become a permanent retoucher of photographs, and lived at Levallois with a mistress by whom he had a son. The meeting of the two artists was extremely cordial. How well family affections can be maintained at a distance! The day after this meeting, you might have thought father and son had never been apart. Invited to Levallois, Ambert had made the acquaintance of his father's new family, and the food was so good and the mistress so charming that, when they offered him a room, he accepted and now lived there permanently as the son of the house. But this piece of good luck had its uses. It so happened that, one Sunday, having left Jeanne and her mother rather late, I reached the Gare Saint-Lazare to find the last train gone, and had no other resource than to return to the Faubourg Saint-Jacques. Since her son's bed was vacant, Mme Ambert was naturally obliged to offer it to me, and I slept in her house for the first time. This satisfactory first step taken, the rest soon followed. From then on, instead of going there only on Sunday mornings, I went on Saturday evenings, straight from the office, to return only on Monday morning. I was thus on the spot earlier and more comfortably to take advantage with Jeanne of the marketing period on Sunday mornings. But, indeed, did we still require that period? I must certainly have passed already from Ambert's bed to Jeanne's and I don't think we bothered very much any more. In the end, since my future stepmother still left much to be desired, I had no hesitation in making the heroic decision of going to live permanently in the Faubourg Saint-Jacques with my mistress and her mother. Nor did this have any repercussions in Courbevoie. My father had ceased caring and my future stepmother was much too delighted at having achieved her object. I was even allowed to take with me a little work-table which had belonged to my mother, as well as a little Louis XVI clock, both of which I transported on foot one evening, the clock striking continuously throughout the journey. Thus, barely two months after their leaving the uncle's house, everything had been arranged for the best. If Mme Ambert had lost her son to some extent, she had found another in me, while Jeanne's and my love had at last achieved fulfilment. No effort had been required, it had all come about in the most natural way in the world, and we had even renounced, if only among ourselves, all attempts at saving appearances, which are so deceptive anyway. We were living together like a married couple, neither more nor less, rather more indeed. Jeanne and I shared the same bed, Mme Ambert kept house, and when Ambert chanced to come for the night, there was no need to put up an extra bed for him beside ours. A conspectus of these splendid days will certainly be appreciated. I used to go every morning to *La République Française* and come back each evening. How often have I made that journey by the Rues Saint-Jacques, Gay-Lussac, Monsieur-le-Prince, de l'Ancienne-Comédie and Mazarine, the Pont des Arts, the Avenue de l'Opéra and the Chaussée-d'Antin, as far as No. 42! I can still see the faces of the people whom I invariably met at the same places and at the same times. I still meet some of them on occasions, but they are much changed, have grown so old, a great deal more than I have, it seems to me. For instance, there was, at that time, at 57, Rue Monsieur-le-Prince, a women's lodging-house called the Boléro, of which one of the lodgers, a very good-looking girl whom I used to see on the establishment's doorstep each time I passed, interested me very much. I thought she resembled a little one of Jeanne's aunts, the famous singer. A little fuller in the bust perhaps? The Boléro has since disappeared, but this woman, now a good deal faded, lives in another lodging-house in the Rue de Vaugirard, quite close to the Rue

Corneille. At least, I saw her there as I passed by a little while ago. At six o'clock, I went home. There was no water in the house, and I went immediately to fetch two large bucketfuls from a little drinking-fountain, which still exists, opposite 113, Boulevard de Port-Royal. It seems to me, however, that it was not quite so far from the corner of the Faubourg and it must have been moved when they were building the new houses. I did not mind this chore at all and often I even made several journeys. One feels so well when in love. After dinner we invariably went out for a walk like everyone else. We used to go to the Luxembourg. Mme Ambert would sit on a bench, gossiping happily with acquaintances, those elderly men and women of which every district has its peculiar collection, while Jeanne and I took our love for a stroll apart. Or we went to sit in the Place de l'Observatoire, which still had great charm at that time, without the station and the Garnier of today, and with the old café of the Closerie des Lilas, not ugly and gawdy as now, and the statue of Marshal Ney on the other side, under the trees, in front of Bullier, which was also less vulgarly glittering then. The Place de l'Observatoire was still as it is described in one of M. Coppée's poems. But all that district has changed much since then. The Rue Saint-Jacques, not yet widened and without the utilitarian buildings of the Nouvelle Sorbonne, was still a picturesque old street throughout its length. The Boulevard Saint-Michel itself, the least Parisian place in Paris, had still quite a character of its own, which it has since lost thanks to the cafés and so-called fashionable shops there now. Besides, you were not deafened, as you are today, by the hideous mechanical tramways and the noise of the Sceaux underground railway. On the Place de la Taverne du

Panthéon, there was a big draper's shop, Aux Galeries du Panthéon, which was certainly no more ugly than what has replaced it. What changes have taken place there in particular! There is no longer anything interesting to be seen. On the contrary, the women are always the same. It seems to me, too, that the Luxembourg was then less full of all that pretentious art-student scum with their hideous women, which has prevented my ever setting foot in it any more. Finally, the whole district, the Luxembourg included, was not encumbered as it is today by all those bits of variegated masonry one knows so well, from the *Penseur* with his famished air and the chemists *Pelletier* and *Caventou*, to *Le Play* and *Leconte de Lisle*, not forgetting the *Chopins*, the *Sainte-Beuves*, the *Augiers* and other *Comtes*. Yes, it has all much changed. And I have, too. To realise it, I have but to remember my Sundays at that time. What a joy those Sundays were! I should certainly be no match for them today. You are not always young. A day comes when you have to sober down. But when I recollect how I enjoyed myself, I am not a little proud of it. On those days, we used to leave Mme Ambert at home, which was a considerable joy in itself. And Jeanne and I would go and walk round the bandstand in the Luxembourg several times, a practice it would seem some people never grow tired of, for I still on occasion see through the railings figures dating back to that period and still walking round. I can see myself pretty well as I was then, clean-shaven, dressed entirely in black, while Jeanne, on the contrary, wore light dresses and positively dazzling hats. Or we would go for an hour to the Concerts-Rouge, then at the corner of the Rue Gay-Lussac and the Boulevard Saint-Michel, where the new Sceaux station stands today, which at the least has the merit of making less noise. I remember seeing there a young violinist, seventeen at most, with an enchanting face I never tired of watching. Then, dinner, and off we went again. I had remained on fairly good terms with my father and had his tickets every Sunday, so we went to the Comédie, having the same two seats in the dress-circle each time, those nearest the stage, on the right as you look at it, in the second row. And there, almost every Sunday for nearly two years, I formed my mind by listening to the superb nonsense recited in so false a tone and with such a ridiculous air by the great artists we know so well. Fortunately, these plays, like the great books I read for so long, served merely to strengthen, little by little, my passionate and exclusive taste for myself. On one occasion, Jeanne wanted to see the ladies and gentlemen of the company close to from the prompter's box; my father agreed and was so amiable towards her, while I remained in the auditorium, that for a moment I felt quite anxious. And to palliate these excesses, let me sigh for a moment in recollection of our tender transports in that single uncomfortable room, in which our bed touched that of Mme Ambert—did she hear? or did she not?—who, in any case, never seemed to be aware of them and never made any allusion to them. Nevertheless, though I was only eighteen, I was already dreaming of making love somewhat differently. Nothing shocking or perverse, of course. . . . How many other details and memories of every kind I retain of this first great passion! Jeanne's astonishing resemblance to the women of the Chéret posters, which were then at the height of their renown. The evenings on which I attempted to work, paper spread out before me, but without success; no doubt I was waiting for inspiration in which, I presume, I

228

still believed at that time. But I did not lose my head in spite of my love. One Sunday, Jeanne, being ill, was obliged to remain in bed. Her groans bored me to death, and I could think of nothing better to do than go out for a walk, to return only in the evening. I remember, too, the songs she sang though she never knew all the words of any of them. One, of which I remember the tune, began thus:

> Je ne songeais pas à Rose;
> Rose au bois vint avec moi,
> Nous parlions de quelque chose,
> Mais je ne sais plus de quoi . . .

And another, a love-song in the grand style, and much more to the purpose, ran something like this: *Si tu m'aimes, si l'ombre de ma vie* . . . I can still hear her way of singing them, particularly the first, the syllables clearly and separately enunciated, her voice rather grave, a little husky, the kind of voice that has always moved me. Indeed, yes! And I can see her amusing herself, as she frequently did, by doing the splits in series, rather well too, quite like a clown. And the door-mats and milk-bottles she changed from floor to floor in the houses we visited, and the apples she lifted from the stalls! I have alluded to this in *Le Petit Ami* in a passage I wrote about her at the period of my great grief. In the meantime, like her brother, she had made acquaintance with her father again, had been several times to Levallois, and I had gone there too in the end. Ambert had started out on his high destiny. He had left the School of Decorative Art and was now working in the same firm as his father, in the Boulevard des Capucines, at retouching photographs. At the same time, it had occurred to him to become an actor, and he was preparing himself assiduously for the Conservatoire examination. He always carried about with him in his pockets the texts of masterpieces, of which he learned merely a single scene of a single part, not bothering with the rest—just as they do in the Faubourg Poissonnière—which is of course excellent training for interpreting a complete character in a play. Nor had he neglected his success with women. He had barely been at Levallois for a year before he became the lover of his father's mistress. This highly fastidious romance had begun, moreover, in a singularly touching way. Having fallen rather seriously ill with typhoid, Ambert had been bed-ridden at Levallois for several months; and had been nursed with great devotion by his father's mistress, who was called Laure, and is the only person of all that world I still see from time to time. Laure, at that time, was between thirty and thirty-five and was still quite pretty. On his side, Ambert was so prepossessing, so very much what women consider a fascinating fellow! He had no particular distinction, but what is much more valuable, an appearance of physical strength, and an admirable way of making eyes at them, inviting them to a charming interlude in bed. The circumstances had done the rest, and by dint of being there alone together for several months, with all the intimacies of the sick-room, they ended by falling into each other's arms. The early days of Ambert's convalescence were quite a love-poem. As soon as his father left in the morning, he took his place in his bed and there completed this latest conquest which his fine phrases, languishing glances and interesting air had earned him. And, since then, the liaison had continued, without the father suspecting anything, any more than he did my love-affair with his daughter, which

Laure alone knew about from the confidences Ambert had made to her. In agreement with their father, Jeanne and Ambert called Laure 'aunt'. This simplified things and avoided all embarrassment. And how we enjoyed ourselves! Jeanne had found a job in a firm that did Russian embroidery in the Boulevard Haussmann. I often used to meet her at Saint-Augustin, after office hours, and we would go and dine at Levallois with Ambert, his father, Laure and Laure's young son, aged seven, Ambert's and Jeanne's half-brother, and sometimes Ambert would come back with us to visit his admirable mother. What a gay and amusing journey we three used to have on top of the omnibus from the Panthéon to the Place Courcelles! Nor were the evenings spent together at Levallois any less entertaining. After dinner, Ambert and his father would talk knowledgeably of art. M. Ambert would tell of his youth, his old dreams of fame, when he had wanted to follow in his father's, the opera singer's, footsteps, and to rival his two sisters who sang in comic opera and, finally, rising on his son's demand, would sing some booming air: *Plus blanche que la blanche hermine* . . . which had been his great piece in the old days. The man was choked by his own talent, and afterwards had to go out on to the balcony to get a breath of air to recover himself. What quick kisses there were then between Ambert and Laure! At first, Ambert was not very sure of my feelings and he thought it necessary one evening to sound me out and explain the situation. His father was an artist, his mother had never been able to rise to his level, and so the marriage had broken up. Wasn't that like a good son? I did not want to lag behind him and replied at once that I was of his opinion, that I understood very well that his mother had been abandoned not only once but twice.

Youth sometimes has its perceptions. But my most personal memory is of going to luncheon at Levallois with Jeanne on a week-day. Ambert and his father were at their work in Paris. We were alone with Laure and her son. After luncheon, as the child was going to school, Laure went into another room to get him ready and left us alone for a few minutes in the dining-room. Jeanne, throwing her napkin down, insisted on making love on the spot, without more ado, and as she immediately lay down on the floor with her skirts raised, I had her in a couple of minutes. . . . Poor sweet darling, she is today a huge bourgeoise, married, a materfamilias of principle. Will she ever read what I have written of that brilliant period? And even if she does read it, will she be moved? And yet, it's all her youth too!

My first love will certainly occupy as great a place in this book as in my heart. But, before going on, I must say a few words about two friends, with whom I spent a lot of time at this period. On this subject you may even come to congratulate me on the blessings of friendship. I have been wondering how to set about writing of them, but I can find no solution, and this passage will certainly be of no great value. Since, however, I dislike delaying over a manuscript, I shall take the risk, come what may. Of these two friends, Van Bever, whom I have already mentioned, is alone alive today, and he is so accustomed to people's lack of talent that I shall not surprise him. How I should like to have the time to devote a whole chapter to this friendship which has lasted for nearly twenty-four years! We are both the same age, and I first knew Van Bever at Courbevoie in about 1883, then, having lost sight of him for a while, I met him again, taking the train each morning to Paris like myself, during the final period of my living with my father and when I used to travel up with Ambert. Van Bever was already a writer at this time, and I sometimes think that, to make a profession of writing, I ought to have made up my mind to it then and followed his example instead of waiting so long. Had I done so, I might by now have been as well known as he is, instead of being so far from it. It is true, however, that this would not have prevented his being my senior in the profession of literature. For, indeed, nothing is more difficult than not to have seniors in literature. It is not as a writer that one can sing, as in the *Marseillaise*: 'We shall enter the career when our seniors are no longer there.' For the seniors, on the contrary, are always there, and even the ancestors, M. Catulle Mendès for instance. As for Van Bever, I know few examples of such literary precocity. By the age of eleven, he was already all that he is today. We went to the same school, where he was one class ahead of me, and he was already writing and talking literature quite as well as he does now. The only difference was in the type of thing he wrote. In those days, he was concerned with plays, immense sombre tragedies, which he wrote after school, in secret from his family. What authority it gives one to discover one's vocation so young! Van Bever may have changed his style and devoted himself to less turgid works. But the start he gained over me when we were still schoolboys has remained: I have barely written two books, while his list of 'works by the same author' is almost a pamphlet in itself. When I met him again in the circumstances I have described, and he got to know Ambert at the same time, Van Bever was temporarily shining in journalism as the editor of a little newspaper at Courbevoie, in which he was violently attacking the mayor of the place, a good chemist called Rolland, who died of it soon after-wards what's more. He had made the acquaintance of a young Lyonnais called Pierre Gaillard, a boy of the same age as ourselves, who had recently come to live at Courbevoie with an elderly female relation. Pierre Gaillard, who died three or four years ago, after having written some inimitable things, rather in the style of Maizeroy or Esparbès, was also a young writer who already had to his credit an adaptation in verse of Goethe's *Faust* and a considerable stock of poems. A controversialist of Van Bever's stature immediately acquired a certain prestige in his eyes. While he himself, owing to the fact that he had put *Faust* into French verse, seemed to Van Bever a suitable friend, and they soon became inseparable, spending their time in discussing literature, as if that could serve any useful purpose. Having presented these characters, you will now hear of the destruction of all that sweet happiness I have described above. 'It is very difficult to break things off when you no longer love,' La Rochefoucauld has said. Jeanne and I still adored each other, and it happened quickly, merely taking a whole year. I did all I could, it is true, circumstances took a hand, and Van Bever and Gaillard also helped considerably, without however having the slightest idea they were doing so, neither of them being recipients of my confidences. Suddenly feeling an immense desire for freedom, I began by resigning from *La République Française*, which was a splendid idea, apart from the fact that it was my only source of livelihood. This happened, I think, in about June or July, 1890. Seeing me free, Van Bever determined at once to introduce me to Gaillard, whom he thought more and more exceptional and destined for the greatest of futures. Moreover, it was quite incredible the number of people Van Bever introduced me to over a period of ten years on the pretext that they were destined for great futures in the various branches of art, and who have since become tradesmen or provincial employees. One day, he would come, bubbling over, to tell me of some remarkable chap whom I must absolutely get to know. I always agreed, and he would either bring his protégé to see me or take me to see him, and a week later Van Bever would come back and declare with equal warmth that the protégé was a complete moron and deserved at best to rot in a basement. However, it was decided that I should be introduced to Gaillard and, since Ambert was invited too, we both set out for Courbevoie. We really spent a delightful day in the little parlour in the Rue Carle-Hébert, where the chickens walked in and out, clucking as if quite at home. Under the presiding genius of his elderly relation, and in the presence of us three, who listened with all the air of experts, Ambert in declamation, Van Bever in drama and I in subtlety of meaning, Gaillard read his *Faust*, all five acts, and when he reached the last line there was a concert of praise and congratulation lasting an hour. Ambert, in particular, could not say enough, seeing himself already in the part of Faust, telling us all that he would be a sensation, and regretting only that the play lacked women. An enormous dinner followed, in Van Bever's private apartments near the quay, and we separated at last in the early morning. How should such transcendent pleasures not be repeated? Jeanne was still in her Russian embroidery shop, leaving in the morning and returning at night, of the two of us being now the only one who bothered to go home. In the meantime, I idled about, or went to call on my friends, exactly as if I had a private income. Happy friends, to whom I gave so much of my life at this period, to the detriment of my perfect love, which was fading little by little without my noticing it. How many literary discussions did I not listen to at Courbevoie between Gaillard and Van Bever? I used also to go to Levallois, and listen to Ambert declaiming endlessly from morning till night because of the Conservatoire examination which was drawing near, though this did not prevent his repeating incessantly that, with his voice, he could enter for the singing examination just as successfully. Everyone was working; I alone was without a goal. The theatre and literature interested me equally, but I got no further than mere interest; I was incapable of the slightest effort and preferred meantime to sleep as much as I could. And how I could sleep in those days! It did not matter in the least what the bed was like, and I could easily have slept for a week on end; indeed, I spent most of my time sleeping when I was not out seeing my friends, unless I went for a walk in Paris, which I have always been crazy about doing. I believe, however, that at one moment I had an impulse to take the Conservatoire examination, like Ambert. The contagion of talent, no doubt. When one is young, to hear someone declaiming and gesticulating in imitation of our best actors is very infectious. Each week, too, Van Bever and I met, always at the same place, at the corner of the Boulevard Saint-Michel and the Rue Soufflot, and we went for a long literary walk. His work was covering a wider and wider field, tragedies, comedies, sketches, novels, criticism and newspaper articles, all of which merely needed printing. He was always ahead of me, as I have said, and his days were ceaselessly devoted to achieving fame.

Then, at the end of the year, there were considerable

changes. I do not know what was the cause of it, but since I had been seeing more of her, Mme Ambert had become even more admirable than before, and since frankness is the privilege of youth and I was beginning to have enough of being saddled with all these people, I did not conceal from the stout lady what I thought of her remarkable lack of intelligence. There followed such lamentations that, far from making me relent, I jeered all the more, and decided, in spite of Jeanne's tears and entreaties, to go and live by myself elsewhere, in a place of my very own. In any case, Mme Ambert herself wanted to move. We should all move at the same time. With Jeanne's help, therefore, I set about looking for a room, and my choice soon fell on a big room on the sixth floor at 14, Rue Monsieur-le Prince, while Mme Ambert took a lodging in the Rue Saint-Jacques, almost at the corner of the Rue Gay-Lussac, next door to a sort of convent which still exists. All this happened in January, 1891. The Rue Monsieur-le-Prince, where it joins the Boulevard Saint-Michel, then still had the old wooden railings such as can be seen in an illustration in *Rois en exil* instead of the iron ones of today. I had found a little job on the newspaper *le Siècle*, in the Rue Chauchat, with freedom to go there when I liked. I was beginning a new life and I shall describe it very quickly, regretfully passing over many details. The inauguration of my new bed, for instance, as soon as the carrier who brought it had departed. Jeanne insisted on indulging these pleasures at once. Whether it was the means she employed in bringing me up to scratch that night, or whether, lying there naked. . . . Really, I lose the serenity so necessary to great literature when I recollect these things. It was in this room that I made my first attempt at literature, to the extent of at least a hundred verses a day, written with really limitless inspiration and all torn up when I left Rue Monsieur-le-Prince. Despite his talent, Ambert had failed at the Conservatoire and had gone back to working at retouching photographs for another firm, near the Rue Cadet. Levallois existed no longer. Had M. Ambert eventually found out that Laure was deceiving him with his son or, very much a womaniser himself, had he fallen in love with another mistress, perhaps the one with whom he lives today, or was it both the one and the other? But, one fine evening, he failed to come home, deserted a woman and a child for the second time, and no one could discover where he was or what had happened to him. Luckily for Laure, Ambert was a gallant young man, who knew how to unite the practical with the agreeable. He talked to his mother, who probably had no idea what it was all about, Laure came to see her, the two women fell on each other's necks in their common misfortune and, a month later, Laure and her son came to live in the Rue Saint-Jacques, a few houses lower down than Mme Ambert. During the day, they all lived a communal family life, the ex-wife, the ex-mistress and the son-lover, and in the evening Ambert and Laure went home like a Romeo and a Juliet. As far as we were concerned, Jeanne and I went our own way, and a cheap way at that. We spent the evenings together, and every Saturday night she came round and we made love and were together till the following night. I did my best to vary the programme, however. I would often receive a telegram from Gaillard on the Sunday morning, saying he was expecting me at Courbevoie with Van Bever, and I would leave her at once, paying no attention whatever to her expostulations. And she had to go back to her mother instead of spending a day making love.

What must have been her thoughts at this time, encouraged as she was in secret by Laure and Ambert, who disapproved of her liaison ? Pretty as she was, she could so easily have done better for herself. Oh, certainly, my stock was beginning to fall, and it was not because she loved me less, in spite of everything, but simply because time was passing, and life was there and she wanted to live it. At the time, I did not grasp these high matters. Even if I had, the probability is that it would have changed nothing. In a short space of time, my character had completely altered. I could think of nothing but writing, and of living and dreaming alone. Love took only second place. I went even so far as to sacrifice the remains of our intimacy to friendship, and to be concerned only with my own pleasure. For it was at this period that Van Bever came to stay with me for some time, approximately from May to July. Jeanne then had only Saturdays, when I sent Van Bever to sleep elsewhere, reorganising things for our love-making, and also a Sunday from time to time, when my great-men-to-be did not invite me to Courbevoie. There again, what must she have thought! Since I never really knew, I would just as soon give a few short details about my life with Van Bever during those two months. The rest will be for later, when I write a literary study about myself, which is the best way of getting things accurate. Van Bever remembers very well his arrival one evening at Rue Monsieur-le-Prince, at about six o'clock. I was not at home, and he had to come to look for me at a little greengrocer's at No. 26 in the same street, where I sometimes took my meals. The greengrocer was, so it appears, asking me what was meant by *'une chose béante'* ? Van Bever, who had already an extensive knowledge of the French language, at once joined in the conversation. '*Une chose béante* . . .' he said, 'is something deep.'* But the greengrocer was unconvinced, having no idea of the intelligent fellow he was dealing with. 'All right,' he said, 'let's look it up in *Larousse*!' And the argument went on between them, while I finished my dinner. You can have no idea of the number of books and papers Van Bever took about with him, the complete works of Voltaire, Rollin, Villemain, Millevoye, la Harpe, etc., with the manuscripts of his own works, complete too. I had already a horror of quantities of books and papers, and as soon as we got home, my first care was to throw them all methodically out of the window in spite of his expostulations. In the morning, his books and papers were scattered all over the street, which brought down on my head the censure of the concierge. After that, the two months went by without any particular incident. Every day, at about one o'clock, we went out, and walked soberly to a little restaurant in the Rue de l'Ancienne-Comédie, where we drank innumerable chocolates, seven or eight sometimes. The luncheon hour was over, and we had the whole staff to attend to us. One day, we tried to get credit, which was refused us with considerable alacrity. Then Van Bever would drag me off to the quays, to search for hours among the book-sellers' boxes while I waited for him, having never had that particular taste nor indeed the necessary patience, and we returned home laden with books, which had to be exchanged or sold after they had been read. We used also to spend hours under the galleries of the Odéon, to keep in touch. I have just stopped here for a good quarter of an hour's reflection. After all, why not admit it, in spite of the strait-laced? A great frenzy to read had come over

* *Béant:* gaping, open-mouthed, yawning. *Translator's note.*

me, an immense curiosity, a desire to know and learn everything, and many admirable passages have been written about this. The only thing was that I refused to let myself be embarrassed by lack of money, nor have I ever been able to tolerate the frequenters of libraries. So when I had real need of a book, I stole it, just that. This occurred two or three times, and it was thus that one day, when I had been glancing through *La Vie de Jésus*, in the sixty centimes edition, I could not resist the temptation and left the galleries with the volume in my pocket in order to be able to read it at home at my ease, to the great scandal of Van Bever who, as he said, did not care for that particular sort of literature. In the evening, in my room, we spent our time drinking cup after cup of coffee, Van Bever smoking an enormous pipe whose bowl was carved in the shape of the head of Voltaire, and by midnight we felt so awake we used to go out and walk round and round the Luxembourg before going to bed. When I had any money, I would do Van Bever a courtesy, invariably the same one. I used to lead him to a hairdresser and, despite his protests, have him seized by the assistant and give orders for his hair to be cut short. I often ruined myself in this way. They never cut enough off. To get a satisfactory result, I should have had to take him round every hairdresser in the district the same day. Moreover, we rivalled each other in elegance. Van Bever had at that time black and white check trousers, and freshened up the pattern every morning with the aid of a paint-brush and two little cakes of paint, which finally lent the garment a somewhat British stiffness. As for me, always so hard on my shoes, I believe I was really never better shod than I was then, when I had an admirable pair of Molière period shoes with silver buckles, which my father had used when playing in repertory and which I had carried away from the house one day when he was feeling particularly generous.

In the lodging above my room lived an old man called Guérin, who had private means and with whom we got on very well. He had coveted an old gun I had and I had given it to him, and from time to time he invited us to luncheon. When he omitted this duty for too long, Van Bever would remind him of it by shouting at the top of his voice out of the window. We used to find him in company with an extraordinarily effeminate little fellow, whom he called his nephew, but who was a sort of catamite with whom he no doubt took his pleasure. I still often see this creature in the neighbourhood of the Gare Montparnesse, always walking along with tight little steps and making as much play with his behind as a young cocotte. The room next to mine was occupied by a pretty young housemaid, whom Van Bever was courting. One evening, as we were coming in, he thought he recognised the object of his attachment in a woman climbing the stairs in front of him. He dashed forward, seized her by the waist, and was about to kiss her, when she suddenly turned round to reveal the face of the concierge's wife, aghast with astonishment. From that day, Van Bever's reputation in the house was one of licentiousness, the concierge always looked at him with a glint of jealousy in his eye, while our disillusioned neighbour would no longer listen to his declarations.

I remember, too, how Van Bever thought but little of the verses I produced with so much enthusiasm. He had glanced at them from time to time and, already endowed as he was with a great critical sense, he did not conceal from me, one day, that I was not born to write and would do better to give it up. But counsellors are not payers, as the proverb says. Jeanne had little by little got to know him, and when we went every Tuesday, a red-letter day, to the Montparnasse theatre, where I always had seats through the manager, M. Hartmann, an old friend of my father, he came with us. One evening, we even arranged with M. Paul Albert, M. Hartmann's partner, to collaborate in writing a vaudeville for him, a great project which fell through. How delighted Van Bever will be to relive that period by reading of it. I would talk to him about it from time to time, if he did not become so sentimental as to make the conversation impossible.

I must say two words, in passing, about an opportunity deliberately missed at this period. It concerned a night spent with Gaillard's sister, a very dark young woman of some thirty years of age, who had recently come up from the provinces, and on whom it must be believed I had made a certain impression. For she amused herself by defying me to spend a night beside a woman without touching her, and generously offered herself for the experiment. It was not to know me, were I a simpleton or full of impudence. The experiment took place, in that same Hôtel de Lisbonne of which I have spoken, and she left the next morning without my having even kissed her. But we must take a generous view of women! Had I taken her, she would have been outraged and yet, merely because I kept my word, she called me every name under the sun.

At the end of June, Van Bever left me, and Jeanne and I recovered a few days of real intimacy, the very last. The end of our romance was indeed in sight. Another year of making love in secret and by arranging assignations, and it would all be over. I continued to have so very little money, since I soon lost my job on the *Siècle*, owing to the fact I never went there. In the end, things simply had to be wound up. My father was urging me to enlist, assuring me I was wrong in thinking that my short sight would prevent my being taken, and he made a thousand promises of all the things he would do for me. Jeanne, whom I consulted, said neither yes nor no, except that she pointed out we should be no more separated than we were already, and so, ill-supported by her, for she had a plan of her own, and lacking energy to resist, I ended by giving way. I shall not linger over my father's charming behaviour towards me in these circumstances. After the eulogy I have made him, I have no wish to overwhelm him with bouquets of flowers. Those that garnish the gracious garden under which he lies must suffice him. When I had finally agreed, he invited me to return to his house, and I left the Rue Monsieur-le-Prince. It was at the end of July or during the first days of August. Jeanne had just taken a room apart from her mother, at 7, Rue des Feuillantines, simply to be more free, she assured me, and she quickly transferred my furniture there. The sweet darling was preparing a surprise for me! Nor had I any idea of it, I must say. And I was no less deceived in my suburb, for I learned later from my future stepmother that my father had told her to feed me up and to refuse me nothing, that I might become a strong fellow who would surely be taken for a soldier. The good man wanted to get rid of me by sending me to languish in the provinces, at Montargis, I think. He had already fixed everything to that end. But one evening, when I was talking things over with him, he was unwise enough to reveal the falsity of the promises he had made me before witnesses, and he had to give up his dream, as I had my stay in the country, for, indeed, he invited me to get out again the following morning. I had to find a lodging however. Should I go back to Jeanne? I cannot now remember whether the idea even occurred to me. Since returning to my father's house, I had seen Gaillard nearly every day. I told him the whole story. He knew the commanding officer of a battalion of Chasseurs à Pied, who were in garrison in Courbevoie itself. He told him about me. It was agreed that the medical officer would examine me only for the look of the thing. I made the necessary application and, on the 20th October, 1891, at ten o'clock at night, I entered the barracks at Courbevoie on a three years' enlistment.

I shall not say much about the seven months I spent in uniform, then to discard it for ever. I have never much enjoyed accounts of life in barracks, even in M. Courteline's books, which seem to me pretty boring. My captain was a sympathetic drunkard, whose mental capacity extended no further than the clothing-store, and who one day saved me from a good deal of trouble for having expressed aloud my opinion concerning excessive zeal in the service. Nor must I forget M. Walsin-Esterhazy, since famous owing to the Dreyfus case, who was captain and adjutant of my battalion. I can still see him, on inspection days, when all the officers assembled in the courtyard round the commanding officer, standing alone and a little apart from the rest, haughty and disdainful. I had an interview with him one day, as a result of a protest I had made on the failure of my candidature for promotion owing to short sight and ill-health, and I have rarely met an officer so charming, simple and polite. Together with Major Moty, of whom I will speak further on, these are the only good memories I have as a warrior. Not that I ever had much ambition to become a general.

245

My sole preoccupation was leave. And, indeed, I regularly had leave every Saturday night till Sunday midnight. Only once, at Christmas, as I had been punished, did I fail to obtain the leave on which I was counting. Three days to spend in Paris with Jeanne! I wanted to kill myself. I had loaded my rifle and was sitting on my bed, when a comrade found me, took the weapon away and went to warn the captain. What a crowd of officers there was round me for the next half-hour! They quickly gave me several days' leave at the New Year. Had I really intended killing myself, would I really have fired? Perhaps. I no longer know. I was so romantic, and those barracks, with every kind of brute in them, were so little agreeable! Yet, when I try to re-capture my real feelings at the time, I think it must have been pure play-acting.

And during all this time, what new adornments there were to my love-affair! Laure's and Ambert's advice had been taken and, since my departure, that of Laure in particular, who persuaded her 'niece' to go on the stage, where she might easily find, so she said, a serious lover to support her, while keeping me at the same time, if she so wished. My dear Jeanne was now in a theatre where they put on spectacular musical-comedies, and sang in the chorus wearing costumes of the least possible complication. Perhaps she had also suddenly felt herself to be an artist, and I had become, without changing my allegiance, the lover of an actress, the dream of so many young men. But why is everything different when one is in love? I had had some perception of this when I learned the news from Mme Ambert, who was always the first to drop a brick, the very day after I had entered the barracks. At first, the agreeable side of it escaped me and I felt nothing but an idiotic sensation of jealousy and chagrin. If I had known then what I was soon to discover, that I had at the same time been promoted into being the *amant de coeur*! Oh, I should have done the same no doubt, resigned myself to my good fortune. Jeanne continued to be so charming and so attentive to me, while the unpleasant shock the turn of events had given me only renewed my ardour. We used to meet every Saturday evening after her performance and go back together to the Rue des Feuillantines. And ardent as I was, the love we made in that room was my only military glory! The following day the theatre claimed her, and I shut myself up there till evening when I went back to my savages at Courbevoie. I can still see that room, its window giving on to the courtyard of the Val-de-Grâce hospital, and Van Bever must remember it too, for he often came to spend the afternoon there with me. Then I was sent from the barracks to Val-de-Grâce myself. It was the end of February. I had to be content merely with Jeanne's visits on Thursdays, which she spent teasing me about my enforced chastity though, if we found ourselves alone in a passage, she would show me her breasts. . . . But this was not the whole extent of her care for me. She wrote to me and sent me money. Oh, I was kept then to some extent! And the money certainly originated with that dear Clozel, the serious lover, to whom I am coming in a minute. It was as good a revenge as another after all. Apart from that, my life as an invalid had nothing very depressing about it. On Sundays, I had a visit from Laure and Mme Ambert, and sometimes also from Van Bever. My amiable father even came once, at five minutes to three, which prevented any mutual effusiveness, since visiting hours came to an end at three o'clock. The rest of the time, I acted as secretary to the major in charge of my ward, Doctor Moty, writing up case-histories, or idled away my time with two or three select patients, or listened to the whole ward shouting in chorus one of the popular songs of the day. Does not this extraordinary song date from this period, February to May, 1892?

> Il est en or, il est en or,
> On dirait qu'il prend son essor,
> C'n'est pas du toc, ni du melchior,
> Comm' la cann' du tambour-major,
> Il est en or, il est en or.

When one has heard it over a period of three months, and during such heroic days, one's mind is adorned by it for the rest of one's life.

It was then, following the example of other patients in the same condition as myself, that I plucked up courage to ask the major for leave. It was a Thursday afternoon at the beginning of April. I had warned Jeanne and she was waiting for me. That afternoon occupies a peculiarly select place in our liaison. When we were behaving again after our pleasures, and I was idling about the room, while she was dressing to go out, I noticed a man's photograph on the mantelpiece. He had the expansive air of an actor about him and looked about forty. A piece of forgetfulness on Jeanne's part, no doubt. It is so difficult for women to think of everything. When I questioned her about her relationship with this young man who held pride of place in her room, I obtained nothing at first but a few un-important details, uttered in a tone of voice she tried to make sound casual. He was a friend, an actor at the theatre, in a word, of no importance at all. She overdid it, and this time I was suspicious. What was the point of telling such silly lies, I asked her. And, as one always does on these occasions, I said wouldn't it be better I should know the truth. It was so much better that Jeanne decided to open her heart to me. I learned that the photograph was of Paul Clozel, the star of her theatre, a buffoon well known for his eunuch's voice and pot-belly and moreover her lover of some months' standing. Oh, all these things I am summarising here, and not concisely enough either, things that have since become so utterly indifferent to me, how they made me suffer that day as I sat saying nothing on a little chair between the window and the mantelpiece! For all that I was wearing uniform, there was no martial air about me. Jeanne had expected a scene, no doubt, and she could not get over my silence. While continuing to dress, she poured out the most emollient excuses and consolations and explained her new idyll to me. From the moment she had gone on the stage, Clozel had been so kind to her, given her advice, lavished attentions on her, etc. And now, he was a real father to her; and what a father! He gave her everything she needed, and merely came to make love to her in the morning from time to time. For he was married and had to be circumspect. But his wife was a whore (naturally); he was going to divorce and would then marry her. She even went so far as to point out that we both had the same Christian name! Her future was at stake, she added, and, if I loved her, I would understand. Besides, it wasn't as if we weren't to go on seeing each other. It would be a little less often, and taking certain precautions, that was all. In spite of the great happiness she was offering me, I felt no better. What she was saying was so superb! A love built on kindness! What a luxury after the usual way one

249

makes friends backstage. An actor sees a woman, whether chorus-girl or figurante, who attracts him, with whom he would be prepared to sleep one or more times according to the scantiness of her costume. He places his hand on her breasts or elsewhere, addresses her in the second person singular straight away, and the liaison has begun. Clozel had behaved precisely like this, one more buffoonery to add to the rest. At these times, moreover, one has a curious faculty of vision. I could see Clozel making the gesture I have described, and to it was added the idea that he came to make love here, in my bed, as I did. . . . Oh, perhaps better than I! . . . Ready to go out at last, Jeanne came to me, took my head in her hands, kissed me, and then produced this supremely consolatory phrase which she may have read somewhere, who knows? 'There, there,' she said, 'all great poets have had an unhappy love-affair. It'll make you work.' Admirable creature, who could foresee my great literary future long before I could myself! Did she absolutely insist on alexandrines though? Except for being a great poet, I shall have done my best, and, after that remark, she really cannot hold my recounting our love-affair against me.

I left with Jeanne, who was going to an assignation with Clozel, and returned to Val-de-Grâce. I pass over being welcomed back as if I were drunk, because of the happy look about me. If the patients thought I felt like laughing, they were wrong. The whole life I was leading had become suddenly more intolerable, beginning with them, and continuing with the thought that sooner or later I should have to go back to my comrades at Courbevoie. Three years of this life, and only six months of it gone! Oh, no, no! Or at least I would try to put a term to it, thanks to my grounds for getting a discharge, of which I was now aware, and I suddenly became energetic and determined, for the first time too, which goes to show that one is never deceived without some benefit to oneself. I asked for an interview with Dr. Moty, who granted it at once. I explained my circumstances to him, the serious ones from the purely military point of view of course; the uselessness of my continuing to serve, that I could never be promoted, that it would be three years wasted and so on, indeed all the things I did not care a damn about. I can still see that excellent man listening to me, with his bearded face and long hair, looking even less military than I did. He must have liked me, I think, or I must have made out a good case—the voice of love!—for he did not let me talk for long. 'In fact, you want to be discharged? . . .' he said. I neither replied yes nor no, merely using vague words so as not to commit myself, leaving my face to express my meaning. 'Very well,' he said, 'we'll see about it.' And see about it he did. I went for an interview with the oculist, who at once gave me the necessary document. Dr. Moty then examined me for my palpitations, and I was in such good form, with all the heart-break I was suffering, that his decision was equally prompt. I had merely to await the next board, which I did patiently enough. What had I to complain of? If one had to be crossed in love, I did very well out of it, for Jeanne, now that I knew where the money came from, sent me all the more. I used to go and look at her window every morning, and when I did not see her and the window remained closed, I knew what it meant. Clozel was there, and my fair mistress, concerned with her future, was bestirring herself on his account. Nor had Jeanne made a mistake when she deceived me. I had already begun working again, spending my afternoons pouring my unhappiness into little poems, or into little pages of prose, which I wrote as best I could on my bedside table amid the din of the ward. What a pity I did not have myself photographed, a hospital poet, in my huge dressing-gown and cotton nightcap, and with my sickly air. It would have been a splendid addition to my iconography. At last, the 14th May arrived. I got into a wagon with other infirm men. Rue Saint-Dominique! It was midday. At three o'clock, I was back again and, though I had seen no single member of the board, I had got my discharge. We had all been crowded naked into a little room. And then someone had shouted from a neighbouring room: 'Léautaud!' I had replied: 'Present!' Then they had shouted: 'Discharged!' The whole ceremony had consisted of those three words. There were still another two or three days for formalities, and then I returned to civilian life. I warned Jeanne, who replied that she was expecting me, and I hurried round to her as soon as I was free. Oh, that was a better afternoon, with its programme of ardour, caresses and melancholy! For, indeed, I was not consoled. So great a despair to come upon me in a single month! Nevertheless, I was at first preoccupied with the joy of being free again. The Clozel business came only afterwards, and indeed it had not been so regrettable in its results, particularly since Jeanne showed such enthusiasm in making up for the past! It was a pity Clozel was not there, if it were merely in the interests of his art. He would certainly have found in it the occasion for a new grimace.

I went back to my father's house the same day, and if anyone was excessively pleased at it, it was certainly not my father, that fireside patriot, whom I found furious over my discharge. 'That I should have a son incapable of being a soldier!' he said despondently. However, since I had not yet reached my majority, he had to make the best of the situation and give me a room, and I began living again. Three days later, clean-shaven once more and with my head a little less bare, there were no longer any visible signs of my having been in the army. At first, I had no other preoccupations but Jeanne, seeing her, and worrying my head about our relations. That poor Clozel deserved sympathy, too, moreover. As soon as Jeanne could be rid of him for a day, she would write to me and I would go and spend it with her. We also often met at night, at about half-past twelve, at the tram-stop from which she went home from the theatre, at the corner of the Rue de l'Abbé-de-l'Epée and the Boulevard Saint-Michel, so that we could be together till the following morning. Once or twice I even went to the beastly theatre with tickets from Clozel, and I can see her still, a pretty creature in an effective costume, in a fairy-like setting, beneath the brilliant lights, and I can still hear the tunes of that wonderful chorus of which she was a part, and I can still see Clozel too, sweating and struggling in his contortions. Hardly four or five days went by without a meeting, and it was up to me to be amiable when I came to surprise her at the tram-stop, and stood hidden in the shadows of the Rue de l'Abbé-de-l'Epée. Jeanne was often accompanied by Clozel, who then turned back, since he had to be cautious because of his wife. I would watch them say goodbye to each other and kiss; then Clozel would go, and Jeanne come towards me. 'Hullo, you here? . . .' she would say when she saw me. 'Yes, of course. . . .' I would reply, and we would go and sleep together once again. I remember Clozel arriving when I was still there one morning. He knocked several times, and we both kept absolutely quiet till he went away again, thinking there was no one in. I would also go and spy on them both after the theatre. They used to go for a few minutes to a café on the Boulevard Sébastopol, the back of which gave on to the Rue Palestro, and they always sat on that side so as to be less likely to be seen. I would watch from outside, through the window, hidden by the curtains inside. Oh, what an Othello I was! All this continued for rather less than a month; then, as her pregnancy advanced, and the theatre closed for the summer, Jeanne left the Rue des Feuillantines to go and live for a time in the country, in the neighbourhood of Paris, with Clozel. Our amours were over, that dear love I have recorded with such care, don't you think? It was to begin again for a few months in the following year, and could even have continued after that if I had set about it the right way. I have preserved many little mementoes of Jeanne and of all that period. To begin with, the dedicated photograph I have told you about, and another, a smaller one, which I always carried about with me in the early days of our love, then yet another, taken at her father's house at Levallois, in which she is dressed as a man, wearing my coat and Ambert's béret, then a few others still dating from the time we lived together in the Faubourg Saint-Jacques, and one more taken at the beginning of her liaison with Clozel. I have also a few knots of ribbon with which she tied up her hair, and even a little lock of intimate hair she gave me laughingly one day to console me at the time of our last meetings; they are all enclosed in a little card-case she also gave me. I must not exaggerate. I have not kept these things altogether intentionally; besides everyone has these sorts of treasures. You put them away in a cupboard and forget about them. When you move house, you find them again when packing up. 'I must chuck that in the fire!' you say to yourself, thinking of your new house. But you are tired and in a hurry, and everything finds a place in the new cupboard. This often goes on throughout a whole life. And you are lucky, too, if, unlike me, you do not set about telling of your loves for, if you do, you can never get rid of the relics. They become part of the original manuscript. I also have a few letters from her, those she wrote to me to Val-de-Grâce about her visits, or when sending me money, then again to Courbevoie, when I had gone back to my father's, to tell me she was free and that I must hasten to her! And, then, the last but one, at the time of her leaving with Clozel, saying how impossible it was to go on seeing each other; she wrote to tell me this and say goodbye, to wish me happiness and ask me to try to forget her. I have just read this letter again. A note in pencil in my handwriting shows that I received it on the 7th June, 1892 at nine o'clock at night, and indeed I can see myself meeting the postman on our garden path and opening the letter at once. How I must have suffered on reading it, and gone quickly back to my room to weep at my ease! It seems to me that I am still suffering, merely from remembering the occasion, and if I did not stick to my work like a limpet. . . . Oh, so it is a fact after all that one always remains sensitive to these things, and that one's old heart still keeps a corner, and the best corner, for them? Nevertheless, I can laugh at this story, and even at that part of my youth which it represents. I have always lived in the future and, despite my habit of writing memoirs, I remain the same today. Perhaps it is merely the thought of the days piling up behind me, and that secret delight in melancholy

255

which has always been mine. A last letter from Jeanne, dated 12th June of the same year, asks me to meet her at her mother's the next night, but I have no recollection of the occasion. What does one memory more or less matter anyway?